Bernardo Bertolucci's

Last Tango in Paris

BERNARDO
BERTOLUCCI'S

Last Tango in Paris

The Screenplay by
Bernardo Bertolucci
and **Franco Arcalli**

With Critical Essays by
Pauline Kael and
Norman Mailer

Plexus, London

PLEXUS, LONDON

All rights reserved including the right
of reproduction in whole or in part in any form
This edition copyright © 1976 by
Plexus Publishing Limited
Copyright © United Artists Corporation MCMLXXII
Published by Plexus Publishing Limited
31A Valetta Road, London W3
First printing 1976

ISBN 0 85965 019 7

'Tango' by Pauline Kael: reprinted by permission
© 1972 by The New Yorker Magazine, Inc.
'Transit to Narcissus' by Norman Mailer: copyright
© 1973 by Norman Mailer. Reprinted by permission
of the author and his agents.

All photographs courtesy United Artists

Manufactured in Great Britain

An Alberto Grimaldi Production

MARLON BRANDO
in
LAST TANGO IN PARIS

A film by Bernardo Bertolucci

with
Maria Schneider
Maria Michi
Giovanna Galletti

and with
Jean-Pierre Léaud

Also starring
Massimo Girotti

Produced by Alberto Grimaldi
Directed by Bernardo Bertolucci

A Co-Production

PEA Produzioni Europee Associate S.A.S.—Rome
Les Productions Artistes Associes S.A.—Paris

UNITED ARTISTS

CONTENTS

INTRODUCTION

by PAULINE KAEL

Bernardo Bertolucci's *Last Tango in Paris* was presented for the first time on the closing night of the New York Film Festival, October 14, 1972; that date should become a landmark in movie history comparable to May 29, 1913—the night *Le Sacre du Printemps* was first performed—in music history. There was no riot, and no one threw anything at the screen, but I think it's fair to say that the audience was in a state of shock, because *Last Tango in Paris* has the same kind of hypnotic excitement as the *Sacre*, the same primitive force, and the same thrusting, jabbing eroticism. The movie breakthrough has finally come. Exploitation films have been supplying mechanized sex—sex as physical stimulant but without any passion or emotional violence. The sex in *Last Tango in Paris* expresses the characters' drives. Marlon Brando, as Paul, is working out his aggression on Jeanne (Maria Schneider), and the physical menace of sexuality that is emotionally charged is such a departure from everything we've come to expect at the movies that there was something almost like fear in the atmosphere of the party in the lobby that followed the screening. Carried along by the sustained excitement of the movie, the audience had given Bertolucci an ovation, but afterward, as individuals, they were quiet. This must be the most powerfully erotic movie ever made, and it may turn out to be the most liberating movie ever made, and so it's probably only natural that an audience, anticipating a voluptuous feast from the man who made *The Conformist*, and confronted with this unexpected sexuality and the new realism it requires of the actors, should go into shock. Bertolucci and Brando have altered the face of an art form. Who was prepared for that?

Many of us had expected eroticism to come to the movies, and some of us had even guessed that it might come from Bertolucci, because he seemed to have the elegance and the richness and the sensuality to make lushly erotic movies. But I think those of us who had speculated about erotic movies had tended to think of them in terms of Terry Southern's deliriously comic novel on the subject, *Blue Movie*; we had expected *artistic* blue movies, talented directors taking over from the *Schlockmeisters* and making sophisticated voyeuristic fantasies that would be gorgeous fun—a real turn-on. What nobody had talked about was a sex film that would churn up everybody's emotions. Bertolucci shows his masterly elegance in *Last Tango in Paris*, but he also reveals a master's substance.

The script (which Bertolucci wrote with Franco Arcalli) is in French and English; it centers on a man's attempt to separate sex from everything else. When his wife commits suicide, Paul, an American living in Paris, tries to get away from his life. He goes to look at an empty flat and meets Jeanne, who is also looking at it. They have sex in an empty room, without knowing anything about each other—not even first names. He rents the flat, and for three days they meet there. She wants to know who he is, but he insists that sex is all that matters. We see both of them (as they don't see each other) in their normal lives—Paul back at the flophouse-hotel his wife owned, Jeanne with her mother, the widow of a colonel, and with her adoring fiancé (Jean-Pierre Léaud), a TV director, who is relentlessly shooting a sixteen-millimeter film about her, a film that is to end in a week with their wedding. Mostly, we see Paul and Jeanne together in the flat as they act out his fantasy of ignorant armies clashing by night, and it *is* warfare—sexual aggression and retreat and battles joined.

The necessity for isolation from the world is, of course, his, not hers. But his life floods in. He brings into this isolation chamber his sexual anger, his glorying in his prowess, and his need to debase her and himself. He demands total subservience to his sexual wishes; this enslavement is for him the sexual truth, the real thing, sex without phoniness. And she is so erotically sensitized by the rounds of lovemaking that she believes him. He goads her and tests her until when he asks if she's ready to eat vomit as a proof of love, she is, and gratefully. He plays out the American male tough-guy sex role—insisting on his power in bed, because that is all the "truth" he knows.

What they go through together in their pressure cooker is an intensified, speeded-up history of the sex relationships of the dominating men and the adoring women who have provided the key sex model of the past few decades—the model that is collapsing. They don't know each other, but their sex isn't "primitive" or "pure"; Paul is the same old Paul, and Jeanne, we gradually see, is also Jeanne, the colonel's daughter. They bring their cultural hangups into sex, so it's the same poisoned sex Strindberg wrote about: a battle of unequally matched partners, asserting whatever dominance they can, seizing any advantage. Inside the flat, his male physical strength and the mythology he has built on it are the primary facts. He pushes his morose, romantic insanity to its limits; he burns through the sickness that his wife's suicide has brought on—the self-doubts, the need to prove himself and torment himself. After three days, his wife is laid out for burial, and he is ready to resume his identity. He gives up the flat: he wants to live normally again, and he wants to love Jeanne as a *person*. But Paul is forty-five, Jeanne is twenty. She lends herself to an orgiastic madness, shares it, and then tries to shake it off—as many another woman has, after a night or a twenty years' night. When they meet in the outside world, Jeanne sees Paul as a washed-up middle-aged man—a man who runs a flophouse.

Much of the movie is American in spirit. Brando's Paul (a former actor and journalist who has been living off his French wife) is like a drunk with a literary turn of mind. He bellows his contempt for hypocrisies and orthodoxies; he keeps trying to shove them all back down other people's throats. His profane humor and self-loathing self-centeredness and street "wisdom" are in the style of the American hardboiled fiction aimed at the masculine-fantasy market, sometimes by writers (often good ones, too) who believe in more than a little of it. Bertolucci has a remarkably unbiased intelligence. Part of the convulsive effect of *Last Tango in Paris* is that we are drawn to Paul's view of society and yet we can't help seeing him as a self-dramatizing, self-pitying clown. Paul believes that his animal noises are more honest than words, and that his obscene vision of things is the way things really are; he's often convincing. After Paul and Jeanne have left the flat, he chases her and persuades her to have a drink at a ballroom holding a tango contest. When we see him drunkenly sprawling on the floor among the bitch-chic mannequin-dancers and then baring his bottom to the woman official who asks him to leave, our mixed emotions may be like those some of us experienced when we watched Norman Mailer put himself in an indefensible position against Gore Vidal on the Dick Cavett show, justifying all the people who were fed up with him. Brando's Paul carries a yoke of masculine pride and aggression across his broad back; he's weighed down by it and hung on it. When Paul is on all fours barking like a crazy man-dog to scare off a Bible salesman who has come to the flat,* he may—to the few who saw Mailer's

* This scene was deleted by the director after the New York Film Festival showing.

Wild 90—be highly reminiscent of Mailer on his hands and knees barking at a German shepherd to provoke it. But Brando's barking extends the terms of his character and the movie, while we are disgusted with Mailer for needing to prove himself by teasing an unwilling accomplice, and his barking throws us outside the terms of his movie.

Realism with the terror of actual experience still alive on the screen—that's what Bertolucci and Brando achieve. It's what Mailer has been trying to get at in his disastrous, ruinously expensive films. He was right about what was needed but hopelessly wrong in how he went about getting it. He tried to pull a new realism out of himself onto film, without a script, depending wholly on improvisation, and he sought to bypass the self-consciousness and fakery of a man acting himself by improvising within a fictional construct—as a gangster in *Wild 90*, as an Irish cop in *Beyond the Law* (the best of them), and as a famous director who is also a possible Presidential candidate in *Maidstone*. In movies, Mailer tried to will a work of art into existence without going through the steps of making it, and his theory of film, a rationale for this willing, sounds plausible until you see the movies, which are like Mailer's shambling bouts of public misbehavior, such as that Cavett show. His movies trusted to inspiration and were stranded when it didn't come. Bertolucci builds a structure that supports improvisation. Everything is prepared, but everything is subject to change, and the whole film is alive with a sense of discovery. Bertolucci builds the characters "on what the actors are in themselves. I never ask them to interpret something preëxistent, except for dialogue—and even that changes a lot." For Bertolucci, the actors "make the characters." And Brando knows how to improvise: it isn't just Brando improvising, it's Brando improvising as Paul. This is certainly similar to what Mailer was trying to do as the gangster and the cop and the movie director, but when Mailer improvises, he expresses only a bit of himself. When Brando improvises within Bertolucci's structure, his full art is realized. His performance is not like Mailer's acting but like Mailer's best writing: intuitive, rapt, princely. On the screen, Brando is our genius as Mailer is our genius in literature. Paul is Rojack's expatriate-failure brother, and Brando goes all the way with him.

We all know that movie actors often merge with their role in a way that stage actors don't, quite, but Brando did it even on the stage. I was in New York when he played his famous small role in *Truckline Cafe* in 1946; arriving late at a performance, and seated in the center of the second row, I looked up and saw what I thought was an actor having a seizure onstage. Embarrassed for him, I lowered my eyes, and it wasn't until the young man who'd brought me grabbed my arm and said, "Watch this guy!" that I realized he was *acting*. I think a lot of people will make my old mistake when they see Brando's performance as Paul; I think some may prefer to make this mistake, so they won't have to recognize how deep down he goes and what he dredges up. Expressing a character's sexuality makes new demands on an actor, and Brando has no trick accent to play with this time, and no putty on his face. It's perfectly apparent that the role was conceived for Brando, using elements of his past as integral parts of the character. Bertolucci wasn't surprised by what Brando did; he was ready to use what Brando brought to the role. And when Brando is a full creative presence on the screen, the realism transcends the simulated actuality of any known style of *cinéma vérité*, because his surface accuracy expresses what's going on underneath. He's an actor: when he shows you something, he lets you know what it means. The torture of seeing Brando—at his worst—in *A Countess from Hong Kong* was that it was a *reductio ad absurdum* of the wastefulness and emasculation (for both sexes) of Hollywood acting; Chaplin, the director, obviously allowed no participation, and Brando was like a miserably obedient soldier going through drill. When you're nothing but an inductee, you have no choice. The excitement of Brando's performance here is in the revelation of how creative screen acting can be. At the simplest level, Brando, by his inflections and rhythms, the right American obscenities, and perhaps an improvised monologue, makes the dialogue his own and makes Paul an authentic American abroad, in a way that an Italian writer-director simply couldn't do without the actor's help. At a more complex level, he helps Bertolucci discover the movie in the process of shooting it, and that's what makes moviemaking an art. What Mailer never understood was that his *macho* thing prevented flexibility and that in terms of his own personality he *couldn't* improvise —he was consciously acting. And he couldn't allow others to improvise, because he was always challenging them to come up with something. Using the tactics he himself compared to "a commando raid on the nature of reality," he was putting a gun to their heads. Lacking the background of a director, he reduced the art of film to the one element of acting, and in his confusion of "existential" acting with improvisation he expected "danger" to be a spur. But acting involves the joy of self-discovery, and to improvise, as actors mean it, is the most instinctive, creative part of acting—to bring out and give form to what you didn't know you had in you; it's the surprise, the "magic" in acting. A director has to be supportive for an actor to feel both secure enough and free enough to reach into himself. Brando here, always listening to an inner voice, must have a direct pipeline to the mystery of character.

Bertolucci has an extravagant gift for sequences that are like arias, and he has given Brando some scenes that really sing. In one, Paul visits his dead wife's lover (Massimo Girotti), who also lives in the run-down hotel, and the two men, in identical bathrobes (gifts from the dead woman), sit side by side and talk. The scene is miraculously basic— a primal scene that has just been discovered. In another, Brando rages at his dead wife, laid out in a bed of flowers, and then, in an excess of tenderness, tries to wipe away the cosmetic mask that defaces her. He has become the least fussy actor. There is nothing extra, no flourishes in these scenes. He purifies the characterization beyond all that: he brings the character a unity of soul. Paul feels so "real" and the character is brought so close that a new dimension in screen acting has been reached. I think that if the actor were anyone but Brando many of us would lower our eyes in confusion.

His first sex act has a boldness that had the audience gasping, and the gasp was caused—in part—by our awareness that this was Marlon Brando doing it, not an unknown actor. In the flat, he wears the white T-shirt of Stanley Kowalski, and he still has the big shoulders and thick-muscled arms. Photographed looking down, he is still tender and poetic; photographed looking up, he is ravaged, like the man in the Francis Bacon painting under the film's opening titles. We are watching *Brando* throughout this movie, with all the feedback that that implies, and his willingness to run the full course with a study of the aggression in masculine sexuality and how the physical strength of men lends credence to the insanity that grows out of it gives the film a larger, tragic dignity. If Brando knows this hell, why should we pretend we don't?

The colors in this movie are late-afternoon orange-beige-browns and pink—the pink of flesh drained of blood, corpse pink. They are so delicately modulated (Vittorio Storaro was the cinematographer, as he was on *The Conformist*) that romance and rot are one; the lyric extravagance of the music (by Gato Barbieri) heightens this effect. Outside the flat, the gray buildings and the noise are certainly modern Paris, and yet the city seems muted. Bertolucci uses a feedback of his own—the feedback of old movies to enrich the imagery and associations. In substance, this is his most American film, yet the shadow of Michel Simon seems to hover over Brando, and the ambience is a tribute to the early crime-of-passion films of Jean Renoir, especially *La Chienne* and *La Bête Humaine*. Léaud, as Tom, the young director, is used as an affectionate take-off on Godard, and the movie that Tom is shooting about Jeanne, his runaway bride, echoes Jean Vigo's *L'Atalante*. Bertolucci's soft focus recalls the thirties films, with their lyrically kind eye for every variety of passion; Marcel Carné comes to mind, as well as the masters who influenced Bertolucci's technique— von Sternberg (the controlled lighting) and Max Ophuls (the tracking camera). The film is utterly beautiful to look at. The virtuosity of Bertolucci's gliding camera style is such that he can show you the hype of the tango-contest scene (with its own echo of *The Conformist*) by stylizing it (the automaton-dancers do wildly fake head turns) and still make it work. He uses the other actors for their associations, too—Girotti, of course, the star of so many Italian films, including *Senso* and *Ossessione*, Visconti's version of *The Postman Always Rings Twice*, and, as Paul's mother-in-law, Maria Michi, the young girl who betrays her lover in *Open City*. As a maid in the hotel (part of a weak, diversionary subplot that is soon dispensed with), Catherine Allegret, with her heart-shaped mouth in a full, childishly beautiful face, is an aching, sweet reminder of her mother, Simone Signoret, in her *Casque d'Or* days. Bertolucci draws upon the movie background of this movie because movies are as active in him as direct experience—perhaps more active, since they may color everything else. Movies are a past we share, and, whether we recognize them or not, the copious associations are at work in the film and we feel them. As Jeanne, Maria Schneider, who has never acted before, is like a bouquet of Renoir's screen heroines and his father's models. She carries the whole history of movie passion in her long legs and baby face.

Maria Schneider's freshness—Jeanne's ingenuous corrupt innocence—gives the film a special radiance. When she lifts her wedding dress to her waist, smiling coquettishly as she exposes her pubic hair, she's in a great film tradition of irresistibly naughty girls. She has a movie face—open to the camera, and yet no more concerned about it than a plant or a kitten. When she speaks in English, she sounds like

Leslie Caron in *An American in Paris,* and she often looks like a plump-cheeked Jane Fonda in her *Barbarella* days. The role is said to have been conceived for Dominique Sanda, who couldn't play it, because she was pregnant, but surely it has been reconceived. With Sanda, a tigress, this sexual battle might have ended in a draw. But the pliable, softly unprincipled Jeanne of Maria Schneider must be the winner: it is the soft ones who defeat man and walk away, consciencelessly. A Strindberg heroine would still be in that flat, battling, or in another flat, battling. But Jeanne is like the adorably sensual bitch-heroines of French films of the twenties and thirties—both shallow and wise. These girls know how to take care of themselves; they know who No. 1 is. Brando's Paul, the essentially naïve outsider, the romantic, is no match for a French bourgeois girl.

Because of legal technicalities, the film must open in Italy before it opens in this country, and so *Last Tango in Paris* is not scheduled to play here until January. There are certain to be detractors, for this movie represents too much of a change for people to accept it easily or gracefully. They'll grab at aesthetic flaws—a florid speech or an oddball scene—in order to dismiss it. Though Americans seem to have lost the capacity for being scandalized, and the Festival audience has probably lost the cultural confidence to admit to being scandalized, it might have been easier on some if they could have thrown things. I've tried to describe the impact of a film that has made the strongest impression on me in almost twenty years of reviewing. This is a movie people will be arguing about, I think, for as long as there are movies. They'll argue about how it is intended, as they argue again now about *The Dance of Death.* It is a movie you can't get out of your system, and I think it will make some people very angry and disgust others. I don't believe that there's *anyone* whose feelings can be totally resolved about the sex scenes and the social attitudes in this film. For the very young, it could be as antipathetic as *L'Avventura* was at first—more so, because it's closer, more realistic, and more emotionally violent. It could embarrass them, and even frighten them. For adults, it's like seeing pieces of your life, and so, of course, you can't resolve your feelings about it—our feelings about life are never resolved. Besides, the biology that is the basis of the "tango" remains.

THE PLAYERS

Bible Salesman	MICHEL DELAHAYE
Miss Blandish	LAURA BETTI
Marcel	MASSIMO GIROTTI
Barge Captain	JEAN LUC BIDEAU
Jeanne's Mother	GITT MAGRINI
Rosa	VERONICA LAZARE
Prostitute	GIOVANNA GALLETTI
Her Customer	ARMAND ABLANALP
President of Tango Jury	MIMI PINSON
Tango Orchestra Leader	RAMON MENDIZABAL

PUBLISHER'S NOTE

Certain scenes, involving some of the above roles,
have been included in this book,
although they were deleted
from the final version of the film.

Bernardo Bertolucci's

Last Tango in Paris

SCENE 1

EXTERIOR: RUE JULES VERNE; DAY

This film begins in movement: Tracking shot backward to precede a man walking at a steady, normal pace, underneath an ornate bridge. While he walks, he looks around and screams a curse into the roar of a train passing overhead.

MAN Fucking God!

It is a January morning, in rush hour. Yet this street is not congested. There is even something lazy about it.

A car passes. It is an exception.

As the man walks forward, his glances rapidly take in sections of buildings—stone balconies, curtained windows, an ornamented façade—a kind of architecture that is aging gracefully.

Footsteps resound. Yet the sidewalk in front of him is deserted. The man turns around. There is no one behind him. The resounding footsteps are his own.

It seems strange, in a big city, to hear your own footsteps.

Then, something happens that is normal, even banal, but that at this moment, in this street, for this man, is something special: an apparition—the silhouette of a woman, nothing more, but for him, an apparition.

She has appeared around a corner of the street, and she is walking toward him, on the same side of the street. She looks at the surroundings, a bit curious, a bit bored.

Twenty feet still separate them, and they are the only two beings alive on the horizon. So they look at each other.

She has a mane of blond hair, long legs in a miniskirt.

He wears no tie, a coat that is a little loose, and he is unshaven.

The distance between them diminishes rapidly. The young woman quickens her pace. Now she no longer looks at the man. She looks at the ground or the wall on her left, slightly embarrassed, annoyed. Why?

Because she has realized that his gaze has settled on her and does not budge. Because she has realized that he's slowed his steps, to get a better look at her, to pro-

long his unabashed inspection of her body and her face.

Something attracts her attention: it's a sign over the door of a building. The young girls reads: "Apartment for rent—fifth floor."

She hesitates. She looks at her watch, looks at the street. The man has disappeared. A few feet farther on there is a bar. The girl enters it.

SCENE 2

The young girl descends the stairs to the basement.

GIRL I'd like a phone slug.

BARTENDER All out. Down back and left.

The phone booth is occupied. She buys a token from the ladies'-room attendant and waits impatiently for her turn.

The door of the booth opens. Inside is the man she saw on the street. The young girl retreats to let him pass, and also to escape his eyes. But the space between them is narrow, and necessarily their eyes meet.

His gaze is empty. It rests on her without seeing her or recognizing her. But only for an instant. He disappears up the steps.

Through the open door of the phone booth, we can hear her voice.

GIRL Hello, mamma, it's me, Jeanne. There's an apartment in Passy I'm going to see. Then I go to meet Tom at the station. I promised him. And . . . yes . . . I'll come by the house. See you later. Kisses, so long.

SCENE 3

The young girl advances in the shadows. She approaches the building's entrance. In front of the cage of an old elevator, there is a wooden door with a square cut out of it. This is the concierge's cubbyhole.

The girl sees an older woman, a large woman with gray, greasy, unkempt hair. Is she reading? It is not clear.

GIRL I've come about the apartment. I saw the sign.

The concierge scarcely turns her head. She wears gray-tinted eyeglasses. She looks at the girl expressionlessly and without interest. Her head is sunk between her shoulders.

CONCIERGE The sign? Well, nobody never tells me anything.

GIRL I would like to see it.

CONCIERGE You want to rent it?

GIRL I don't know yet.

The old woman doesn't seem at all interested in the girl.

CONCIERGE They rent, they sublet, they do what

they want and I'm the last one to know about it. You have a cigarette?

The girl opens her purse and passes a freshly opened packet through the opening. The old lady snatches them up. She lights one, and the rest disappear into her pocket.

CONCIERGE Didn't used to be like that. Go up if you want to. But you'll have to go alone. I'm not moving. I'm afraid of the rats.

She turns to a strip of wood on which a series of keys hang from nails, and looks for one in particular.

CONCIERGE Key's disappeared. It's not here anymore. Lots of strange things happen.

She exhales smoke deeply through her nostrils. Something about her seems petrified, as if she'd been stuck in her niche for centuries.
Suddenly a door opens—the door nearest to the stairway. An empty bottle and a hand emerge. The old woman hears the sound of the bottle being set down. She understands without looking.

CONCIERGE They drink six bottles a day.

The girl has waited long enough. She turns, and has started to walk away when the old woman calls her back.

CONCIERGE Wait, don't go, there must be a duplicate.

She ransacks a drawer under the bench, groping as if she is blind.

CONCIERGE Here it is.

She looks at the key, which she holds in the palm of her hand, without giving it to the girl. Finally she hands it over. Passing the key, the old woman grips the girl's hand. It lasts only a moment. She lets go all of a sudden.

CONCIERGE You're very young, right?

GIRL (*to herself*) She's crazy.

SCENE 4

INTERIOR: APARTMENT; DAY

To see better in the dark entrance hall, the girl leaves the front door completely open. Immobile in the somber entrance, the girl contemplates what must be the living room. The morning light filters through one of the large windows, whose shutters are half closed. She takes several steps into the center of the room. The weather is beautiful, and this empty space is agreeable.

She begins to turn in a circle, letting her gaze run from the window to the light walls, the high ceiling, the floor, and the walls once again.

GIRL Who's there?

She has almost screamed.
On the back wall, farthest from the window, is a vague shape in silhouette.

It is the man from the street and the phone booth, the man she has already met twice. He keeps leaning against the wall, looking at her. The girl stands in front of him, lighted by the window behind her.

GIRL (*smiling*) What a fright! How'd you get in?

MAN Through the door.

GIRL Stupid of me. I left it open, but I didn't hear you come in.

MAN I was already here.

GIRL I beg your pardon?

MAN Before you came . . . I was here.

He dangles a key in front of her eyes. She understands finally, but is still suspicious.

GIRL Ah, the key! So you're the one who took it.

She has her key in her hand. As she puts it into her purse she speaks.

GIRL I had to bribe the concierge . . . These old houses are fascinating.

She looks around carefully, considering the space in practical terms.

GIRL An armchair would be nice near the fireplace.

MAN No, the armchair goes in front of the window.

He is in another room. Stacks of newspapers on the floor, old empty bottles, an old bureau tottering between three legs and the wall. He balances it. An unstable equilibrium, but an equilibrium nevertheless. He pursues the game no further. The bureau returns to its former position. Its broken leg never existed, or else existed only in the mark it left on the floor.

Daylight fills the cracks in the walls. The apartment is filled with the feeling of a former life, former tenants.

GIRL (*offscreen, in a loud voice*) You have an American accent . . . Will you rent it?

MAN And you?

GIRL I don't know.

She has also been trying to reconstruct the former life in this apartment, through an empty picture frame.

GIRL What are you doing?

MAN Here's part of a room . . . as a bonus.

He leans out the window, trying to see the young girl's reflection in the window of the room next door. He sees the line of her body while, motionless, she rubs her neck. Then, she looks at his reflection.

GIRL I wonder who lived here. It looks like it's been empty for a long time.

He continues to stare at her. She moves to avoid his gaze.

Also in the apartment are two telephones sitting on

the floor, things that people can't take with them, plus a bathroom with two antique sinks, and gas ducts in the big kitchen.

The man and the girl roam the apartment, launched in research without results. They cross each other, going from one room to the next, without a glance.

The telephone rings. She picks up the phone in the "spare room," he picks up the one in the living room.

GIRL Do I answer or not?

MAN Hello? . . . No, too late . . . it has already been rented.

Excuses; a click; the caller has hung up.

The girl continues to hold the receiver in her hand. She would have liked to talk to the man, now that there's some distance between them. But she remains silent. He listens to her slightly accelerated breathing over the phone. She hears his breathing too, his presence. Delicately he puts the telephone down on the floor, without hanging up. Then he goes to the door of the bedroom and surprises her, crouched on the floor, with the receiver still to her ear.

As soon as she sees him, she hangs up guiltily. She conceals her resentment by speaking very quickly.

GIRL Well, have you decided? Going to rent it?

MAN Yes . . . I had already decided . . . Now I don't know. Would you like it?

She tries to get up. He takes her hand to help her. Their two hands stay together. This is the contact they have been putting off until now. Their fingers begin to know each other, to tell each other everything, for a very long moment. Then they let go.

GIRL I'd have to think about it.

MAN Think fast.

She watches him disappear through the doorway. She hears his feet cross the hall, then the sound of the front door slamming shut. He must have gone. But the moment she starts to leave, she bumps into him.

GIRL I thought you'd left.

MAN I closed the door.

She can't endure his gaze, and turns her back to him, standing very still. It is a way of giving and refusing to give at the same time.
Suddenly the man grabs her from behind. Then their bodies are searching each other, rolling on the floor. His male body becomes part of hers. Their mouths graze, touch, join, lips harden and soften, teeth search for something to bite.
They make love violently, looking for passages that don't exist through their clothing, rushing like two dogs unable to stop, until the end.
Then they lie there a while, exhausted, one on top of the other.
Finished, she gets up, and he sees her disappear toward the bathroom. He can barely straighten his disheveled clothes, unkempt hair. He gets himself together slowly while he listens to the water running in the bathroom.

SCENE 5

INTERIOR, EXTERIOR: STAIRS AND STREET; DAY

Now the girl is on the landing, waiting for the elevator. The apartment door opens. He leaves in turn. He locks the door while the elevator arrives. They are both calm and modest. He goes down the stairs on foot. She descends in the elevator. They cannot avoid meeting on the ground floor. They walk without looking at each other, in obvious embarrassment.

Just outside the building, she turns to the right, he to the left. Two directions, two different routes for Jeanne and Paul. For those are their names.

SCENE 6

EXTERIOR: GARE ST. LAZARE; DAY

Jeanne is in a hurry. She runs from the taxi at the entrance of the station, on the steps that lead to the platforms. The train should have arrived several seconds ago.

Jeanne pushes through a crowd moving in the opposite direction: people, attendants, suitcases. She gazes at the faces, looking for someone.

She is so tense that she doesn't notice three people following her secretly.

One of them is a cameraman, his eye glued to a 16-mm. camera. The others are a sound man equipped with Nagra and earphones, pointing his microphone to capture background noise, and a scriptgirl.

Suddenly, Jeanne stops short. She gets on tiptoe and waves her hand high in a rapid salute, then runs again in zigzags around the other passengers.

We weren't able to see to whom she waved. And now that she has reached him, we still can't see his face. They are embracing.

Reopening her eyes, the first thing Jeanne sees is the lens of the 16-mm. camera. Not knowing whether to smile or mistrust it, she hides in the man's shoulder.

Finally Tom appears, emerging from the embrace. Almost thirty: black hair, gray eyes set horizontally in a childlike face. Jeanne gestures toward the small film crew.

JEANNE Are they filming us or someone else?

Tom turns to look into the camera. Then he smiles.

TOM Pay attention . . . We're in a film. From now on . . . if I kiss you, that may be for the movie.

Jeanne doesn't understand. Tom caresses her hair.

TOM If I caress your hair, it may just be for the movie.

He picks up his suitcase and takes Jeanne by the arm with his free hand. The camera precedes them.
Jeanne is astounded; Tom is completely at ease. They walk toward the exit. From time to time, the microphone comes into the shot. Tom presses her hand.

TOM If I squeeze your hand, maybe it's just for the movie.

JEANNE Stop it. What's going on? Do you know them? Who are they?

TOM It's a long story. In two words . . . I'm shooting a film *Portrait of a Girl*. I offered it to television. They accepted . . . in three installments. And the girl is you.

Jeanne tries to interrupt him without any success.

JEANNE You're crazy. You should have asked me first.

TOM I liked the idea of starting with some shots of Jeanne, the girl of the portrait, going to pick up her fiancé at the station . . . Yes, I know them. This is my crew.

Jeanne stares at the cameraman filming them, for a moment, and at the sound man recording everything they say. Then she hides her face in Tom's shoulder. She pinches his arm several times.

JEANNE And so, you kiss me . . . knowing it's a film.

She lowers her voice. Some of her words escape the microphone.

JEANNE Coward . . . traitor.

TOM No, you will see, above all it is a love story. You'll see . . . tell me, Jeanne . . . what did you do while I was away?

JEANNE (*ironically*) I thought about you day and night, and I cried. Darling, I can't live without you!

TOM Cut! Fantastic!

The cameraman stops filming. The sound man takes off his earphones. Tom throws himself on Jeanne and kisses her again. This time, he is sincere. He is not acting.

SCENE 7

INTERIOR: HOTEL, AN ANONYMOUS ROOM; DAY

Wallpaper, an old-fashioned wardrobe closet. A bed. A screen of opaque glass hiding a sink and a bathtub. The bathtub faucet is wide open, and water gushes, sliding down the enamel.

A young maid with the eyes of a cat is on her hands and knees scrubbing the tiles with a rag. She looks for bloodstains that might have escaped her. She scratches them with her nails, makes them disappear with the cloth. She seems to be talking to herself.

CATHERINE I should have finished by now . . . but the police didn't let me. We couldn't touch anything. They didn't believe in suicide . . . too much blood all over. They had fun making me reenact. She went there . . . she went here . . . she opened the curtain. I did everything like her.

She throws the rag in a corner next to a large bath-towel, soaked red with blood. She rinses her hands in the water.

CATHERINE The clients awake all night . . . The hotel, full of police . . . They playing around with the blood. All spies! Only questions. If she was sad . . . if she was happy . . . if you fought . . . if you hit each other . . . and how long had you been married . . . and why you didn't have children . . . Pigs . . .

She sits on the edge of the tub and watches the water run.

CATHERINE They got familiar right away. They said "Nervous type, your boss. You know he was a boxer?" So? "That didn't work . . . so he became an actor, then a racketeer on the waterfront in New York." So? "It didn't last long . . . played the bongo drums . . . revolutionary in South America . . . journalist in Japan . . . One day he lands in Tahiti, hangs

around, learns French . . . comes to Paris and then
meets a young woman with money . . . he marries
her . . . and since then . . . what does he do, your
boss? Nothing." I say: can I clean up now? "No,
don't touch anything. Do you really think she killed
herself?" He pushes me in a corner and tries to paw
me.

PAUL (*offscreen*) Why don't you turn the water off?

The voice comes from the direction of the window.

PAUL Maybe right now they're doing the autopsy.

We see Paul from outside the window. He is looking out. What Paul is watching is a window on the other
side of the courtyard, where a young black woman on
her knees is sewing a button on the bluejeans of the
black man standing in front of her, holding a tenor
saxophone in his hand. The girl looks at Paul too.
Camera on Catherine: She is wiping an object with
toilet paper. She brings it to Paul. It is a long, old-
fashioned straight razor.

CATHERINE They told me to return it to you.

PAUL (*offscreen*) It's not mine.

CATHERINE They don't need it any more. They told
me the investigation is over.

From the other side of the court, we see Paul examine the razor. Camera on Paul: He glances at the window, where the black woman bites off the thread of the
button she has sewn on near the crotch of the man.
Then Paul's hands turn off the faucet of the tub.
In the sudden silence, we see the back of Paul's head
leave the room.
After a moment, Catherine comes into close up and
makes a movement that we do not see.
We hear water running again in the bathtub.

SCENE 8

Jeanne stands in front of the door.

She has the key in her hand. She rings the bell. There is nothing left to do but return the key and go away. She rings again. Nobody there. It is almost noon. A door opens a little farther up the staircase.

WOMAN'S VOICE (*offscreen*) And get a quart of milk too.

Footsteps of a young person. The sound grows louder as feet take the steps two at a time.

Jeanne doesn't want to be seen. She puts her key into the lock and quickly opens the door.

As soon as she's inside, she swings the door almost shut, leaving it open a crack. She sees the little boy on his way out. He is only the blur of a red sweater as he hurries past.

Suddenly Jeanne feels eyes on her. She turns quickly, holding the key up as protection. Her alibi is ready: "I only came to return the key." Someone is watching her. It is a black cat, wild and fierce, watching her from the doorway of the living room.

A moment. Then Jeanne explodes. She advances, stamping her feet and hissing through her teeth like a lunatic. The cat disappears into the living room.

When Jeanne appears in that room, she is just in time to watch the cat vanish out the window. Jeanne runs across the room. She looks out the window—peaceful roofs. The cat is beyond her view.

VOICE (*offscreen*) Hello? Hello?

Jeanne wheels around. Once again she holds the key in front of her. A couple of footsteps. Then an armchair appears, an armchair traveling, a foot off the floor, on human legs.

TALL MOVER Okay, where do I put it?

It's the voice of someone who has no desire to wait for an answer.

JEANNE You could have rung the bell.

TALL MOVER Door was open.

Jeanne doesn't know what to say. He puts the armchair down and appears behind it, a cigarette butt between his lips, an exhausted air.

TALL MOVER Can I put it here?

JEANNE No, in front of the fireplace.

The man follows her directions, then walks out. Jeanne would like to leave.
The door is filled by an arm introducing four chairs, one after the other. Another mover enters; this one is short.

SHORT MOVER The chairs?

Jeanne makes a vague gesture. The short mover puts them in a circle.

TALL MOVER What about the table?

She looks around briefly.

JEANNE I don't know. He'll decide.

The short mover notices with disgust the absurdity of arranging chairs around an empty space while a table sits off to one side, deserted.

As they walk away, the girl smiles to herself. The placement is impossible.

She tries once again to leave. There is nothing to do. She must retrace her steps. Now the two men are transporting a box spring complete with mattress. They hold it at each end, occupying the entire corridor, and ask for directions. She makes undecipherable gestures with her hand.

The two arrive in the spare room. We see the bed disappear into the room, but only three-quarters of it. The end of the bed sticks out of the room.

A smile plays quickly across Jeanne's lips. The two movers stand in front of her, waiting.

THE TWO MOVERS Thank you, ma'am.

Although it takes her a minute or two, Jeanne understands. She opens her purse and offers them a bill. They touch their index fingers to the brims of their berets.

As she watches them leave, Jeanne sees Paul enter. His back is to her while he doublelocks the door. There is just enough time for her to retreat to the living room without being seen. We follow Paul into the living room. Jeanne is seated in the armchair, still and falsely

composed. Paul looks at her without surprise, as if her being there is absolutely normal.

PAUL That chair goes in front . . .

He heads for the armchair in which she is sitting, frightened, hugging her knees.

PAUL In front of the window.

Paul pulls the armchair over to the window, with her in it. He arranges it in front of the window, then takes off his jacket and hangs it on the window. His gestures are precise, irreversible.

JEANNE I came to return the key. To return it to *you.*

PAUL What do I care? Take off your coat. Come help me. Take these chairs . . . and put them here . . . Put them on the other side.

She obeys; his tone leaves no other choice. Together they begin to move the table. In the center of it, perfectly in view, is the key that Jeanne brought back. She indicates it with her chin.

JEANNE There it is.

Paul retreats several steps to survey the new position of the table. Then he takes the chairs and passes them to her, one by one.

PAUL Around the table.

She does it, and, looking at the furniture, she speaks.

JEANNE You didn't waste any time.

She puts the last chair in place. When she turns around, the man is no longer there. She goes to the door. She wants to call him, but doesn't know his name.

JEANNE Listen . . . Mister . . . I have to go now.

She advances cautiously toward the spare room with the bed protruding from the doorway.
Paul is there, comically passive before the crushing reality—the room is smaller than the bed.

PAUL The bed is too big for the room.

JEANNE I don't know what to call you.

PAUL I don't have a name.

JEANNE You want to know mine?

She can't finish her phrase. Paul's slap is not very violent . . .

PAUL No! No, I don't—I don't want to know your name. You don't have a name, and I don't have a name either. No names here. Not one name.

. . . but it is completely unexpected. Jeanne doesn't even have time to dodge it. She moves a hand to her cheek.

JEANNE You're crazy!

Tears of rage well up in her eyes. He presses his point.

PAUL You don't have a name. Neither do I. No names.

JEANNE Yes, yes . . . no names. Why?

PAUL Maybe I am. But I don't want to know anything about you. I don't want to know where you live or where you come from. I want to know . . . nothing, nothing! You understand?

JEANNE You scared me.

PAUL Nothing. You and I are going to meet here without knowing anything that goes on outside here.

She has backed up into a corner. He lifts her chin. Then he slides a hand behind her neck.

JEANNE But why?

PAUL Because . . . because we don't need names here. Don't you see. We're going to forget everything we knew—every—all the people, all that we do, all that we—wherever we live. We are going to forget that, everything—everything.

JEANNE But I can't, can you?

PAUL I don't know. Are you scared?

Jeanne takes his hand and carries it up to her eyes. She discovers his wrist, caresses it, studies it.

JEANNE No, not anymore. Not now . . . let me go. I'll come back.

She speaks with her eyes lowered, suddenly timid.

JEANNE Tomorrow . . .

Her lips caress his hand.

JEANNE Please. I'll want it more tomorrow. I want you too much now.

PAUL Yes. That's good. That way it won't become a habit. It's a way of making love.

Paul kisses her, touches her. She loses herself in his shoulder.

JEANNE Don't kiss me. If you kiss me, I won't be able to leave.

PAUL I'll walk you to the door.

They walk with their arms around each other. But, instead of the front door, they are in front of the spare room. Paul sits down on the end of the bed jutting into the hallway. Jeanne disappears into the room. We follow her movements in his expression.

SCENE 9

INTERIOR: PAUL'S ROOM; DAY

Hands rummaging through drawers, under shirts, in the linen, under sweaters. Hands that search night tables next to the double bed, hands that torment the pockets of clothing in the closet. The woman who is searching is about fifty-five years old. She is Paul's mother-in-law.

Paul is in the doorway, leaning against the door-frame. He looks at her without betraying the slightest emotion. As soon as she notices him, the mother stops searching.

MOTHER I thought you would be here.

PAUL I expected you later.

MOTHER I took the first train . . . Paul, how horrible, how horrible.

The stillness is broken by the woman, who moves with extreme fatigue. She goes over and hugs him. The man does not move.

MOTHER Papa's in bed with asthma. The doctor wouldn't let him come.

She tries to leave, but Paul hangs on to her, for a moment, with violence.

MOTHER It's better like this. I'm stronger.

Suddenly the woman has an idea. She goes over to the closet and stands up on tiptoe. She slides her hand over the top shelf.

She finds two or three woman's handbags, and piles them on the bed. One by one she opens them and turns them upside down.

Meanwhile, Paul tries to straighten up after her.

PAUL What are you looking for?

MOTHER Something that would explain . . . A letter, a sign.

PAUL I told you. There's nothing. Absolutely nothing.

There's nothing inside them but a dirty handkerchief, a forgotten lipstick.
The mother sits down on the bed, as if collapsing.

MOTHER It's impossible that my little Rosa . . . nothing for her mother—not even a word.

Paul puts the handbags away. Up above, over the closet there is an old, big suitcase: his. Paul looks at it.

PAUL It's useless to keep looking.

MOTHER Not even for you, her husband.

Paul doesn't answer. He picks up the mother's suitcase, standing near the door; old and worn, it looks very much out of place.

PAUL You need to rest. I think number twelve is empty.

He lets the woman go ahead of him. They walk down a corridor in silence. It is not the corridor of a private house. It is too anonymous, too winding, with too many closed and numbered doors.
They climb the stairs, passing a black couple on the way. Paul meets his mother-in-law's gaze as it leaves the black couple.

MOTHER With a razor?

PAUL Yes.

The woman starts to climb again. They are on the third floor—the corridor. Room Number 12. Paul opens it with a passkey. The room is typical of anonymous, third-rate hotels: a sink, a closet, the bed, all surrounded by old wallpaper. Paul puts the suitcase on the bed.

MOTHER What time did it happen?

PAUL I don't know. At night.

He has no desire to go on talking.

MOTHER And then?

PAUL And then . . . I already told you. When I found her, I called an ambulance.

Paul goes into the corridor. The adjacent door is closed. He puts his ear against it. He hears water running.
Inside the room his mother-in-law opens her suitcase and begins to unpack a few things. She speaks to Paul, thinking he is still listening.

MOTHER After your phone call, we stayed up all night, talking . . . about Rosa and you. Papa kept whispering as if the thing had happened in our house.

She takes her belongings out of the suitcase: a nightgown, bedroom slippers, a black dress.
Then the mother-in-law calls him loudly.

MOTHER Paul!

Paul reappears.

MOTHER Where did it happen?

PAUL In one of the rooms.

MOTHER Did she suffer?

PAUL Ask the doctors. They're doing an autopsy.

MOTHER An autopsy.

Paul turns his back again, and goes to open the neighboring door. The sound of running water becomes

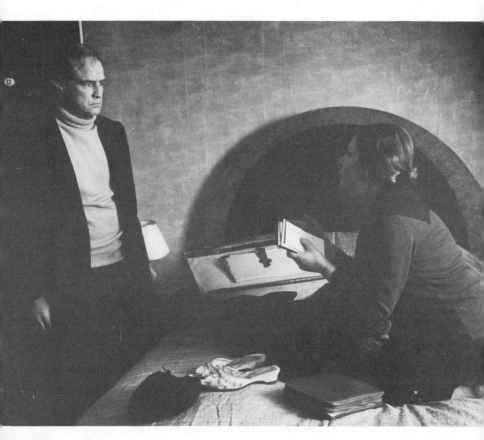

louder. It is possible to see into both rooms at the same time from the corridor—the mother-in-law's room and the one Paul is entering. The bathtub faucet is still open. He bends over to close it.

In her room the mother has extracted a handful of black-rimmed cards and envelopes from the suitcase. She meets the gaze of Paul, who has just reentered the room.

MOTHER I had them in the house. I've been through death before. By now I think of everything. I'm going to make her a beautiful room with flowers everywhere.

PAUL Cards . . . mourning clothes . . . parents . . . flowers . . . all in that suitcase. You've remembered everything. One thing only—I don't want any priests.

MOTHER But, but Paul . . .

PAUL Understand?

The mother gets up.

MOTHER You need them. It must be a religious funeral.

PAUL No! Rosa wasn't a believer. Nobody believes in the fucking God here.

MOTHER Don't shout, Paul! Don't shout like that!

PAUL Priest doesn't want any suicides. Church doesn't want suicides, do they?

MOTHER They'll give her absolution. Absolution and a nice Mass. That's all I ask, Paul. Understand? Rosa . . . She's my baby girl, Rosa.

Then the woman goes immediately to blackmailing, to accusing.

MOTHER Do you know what Papa said? "My little girl was always happy. What did they do to her? Why did she kill herself?"

PAUL Why does one kill oneself? You don't know why, do you? You don't know.

He moves out of the doorway and slams the door shut, leaving his mother-in-law alone. He walks down the hallway. Several doors open slightly. We see slices of faces, the eyes of hotel guests.
Bluntly, he closes whatever doors are ajar.

SCENE 10

INTERIOR: APARTMENT; DAY

We can see the bed jutting out of the spare room. We hear the sound of feet moving.

JEANNE (*offscreen*) I like it because it's healthy exercise—keeps your body in shape and gives you a great appetite.

Jeanne emerges and goes toward the bathroom. She

is wearing only jeans, no shirt or bra. After a moment
Paul follows her. In one hand he carries his shirt, suit,
and socks. When he reaches the bathroom, she slams the
door in his face.

JEANNE (*offscreen*) Leave me alone. There's not even
a key in this door.

PAUL I took it away, let me watch.

JEANNE (*offscreen*) It's not very interesting.

PAUL That depends. Are you peeing?

JEANNE (*offscreen*) No.

PAUL Then you're washing yourself.

Paul begins to laugh softly.

JEANNE (*offscreen*) I'm finished. You can come in
now.

Paul enters. She is putting on her make-up in front
of the mirror. Paul continues chuckling as he turns on
the faucet in the sink. Finally Jeanne turns around.

JEANNE What's so funny?

Paul poises his hands on the edges of the sink and
tests its solidity.

PAUL Nothing. I just pictured you perched on top
of the sink. It takes practice to keep your balance

and wash yourself at the same time. If you fall, you could break a leg.

She is furious. He walks up behind her and kisses her bare shoulders.

PAUL Don't be like that.

Jeanne is suddenly calmer.

JEANNE We're different. There are some things . . . I—I'm ashamed of.

PAUL Forgive me? Sure?

He returns to the sink.

JEANNE Yes.

PAUL Then come here and wash me.

JEANNE Not on your life. What makes you think you can order me around like that.

PAUL You don't know what you're missing.

During this last exchange he's been washing himself, without any help. Modestly, she turns her back.

JEANNE You know what you are? A pig.

PAUL A pig? Me?

JEANNE A toilet is a toilet, and love is love. You mix up the sacred and the profane.

Paul puts on his pants and shirt. He sits on the edge of the tub to put on his socks. He contemplates one foot.

PAUL I once saw a very sad Swedish film that mixed up the sacred and the profane.

JEANNE All pornographic films are sad. They're death.

PAUL It wasn't pornography, it was only Swedish. It was called *Secret Stockholm*. It was the story of a very shy guy who finally got up the courage to invite a girl to his house. While he's waiting . . . all excited, all emotional, he begins wondering if his feet are dirty. He checks. They're disgusting. So he runs into the bathroom to wash them. But there's no water. He's desperate, doesn't know what to do. Suddenly he gets an inspiration. He put his foot in the toilet and flushes.

Jeanne begins to laugh.

PAUL The guy's face lights up. But when he tries to take his foot out of the toilet, he can't. It's stuck. He tries again. He pulls it desperately. No luck. The girl finds him desperate, crying, leaning against the wall, with his foot in the toilet bowl.

At that moment, Jeanne can't keep from laughing any longer.

PAUL He says: "Go away. Don't ever come back." She says: "I can't leave you like this. You'll starve to death." And she goes to get a plumber. The plumber studies the case but doesn't want to take the responsibility. "I can't break the toilet," he says, "it might hurt his foot. Call an ambulance." The attendants arrive with a stretcher, and they all decide to unbolt the toilet from the floor. They put the boy on the stretcher with the toilet on his foot like an enormous shoe. The two attendants begin to giggle. The first slips down the stairs, falls under the stretcher, the toilet falls on his head and kills him instantly.

Jeanne is laughing too hard to put her make up on. Paul, who is dressed, walks out of the bathroom. Alone, Jeanne finishes her make-up.

Paul begins to drag the bed out of the spare room. He pushes it painfully into the hallway.

The bed is in the center of the living room when Jeanne arrives, ready to leave—perfectly combed, perfectly made-up. They look at each other. She waves to him and goes as far as the door. He watches her stop, turn around and stretch out her hand.

Then Paul throws something to her. We follow the key, which flies in a slow trajectory to Jeanne. The girl smiles and disappears. We accompany her.

She walks with a quick, determined stride. At the front door, she turns around and retraces her steps. She reappears in the doorway to the living room.

JEANNE Shall we begin again?

Paul doesn't answer. He begins to unbutton his shirt. She imitates him. They are far from one another, each on one side of the room, and they undress in silence, calmly and naturally. She begins to move toward him slowly, and talks, her eyes lowered.

JEANNE Let's just look at each other.

PAUL Yeah.

JEANNE I want to look at you too.

They kneel in front of each other. They look at each other, explore each other. Paul and Jeanne slowly discover each other's naked body. They exchange few words, barely murmuring.

JEANNE It's beautiful without knowing anything.

PAUL Maybe.

JEANNE Adam and Eve didn't know anything about each other.

PAUL We're like them in reverse. They saw they were naked and were ashamed. We saw we had clothes on and came here to be naked.

JEANNE What you're saying is beautiful.

The silence of the room is broken by the rustling of Paul's body as he slides lightly onto her. Jeanne changes positions, in a long movement, to offer herself to him.

JEANNE Maybe we can come without touching.

PAUL Come without touching? With our eyes . . . and voices . . . You concentrating? Did you come yet?

JEANNE It's difficult.

PAUL I didn't either yet. You're not trying hard enough.

JEANNE I shall have to invent a name for you.

PAUL A name? Oh Jesus Christ! Oh God—I've been called by a million names all my life. I don't want a name. I'm—I'm better off with a grunt or a groan for a name. Do you want to know my name?

He makes an animal noise. Jeanne smiles.

JEANNE It's so masculine. Listen to mine.

She also makes a noise, which seems to come from the bottom of her throat.

JEANNE Do you like it?

PAUL (*laughs*) I—I think it's a last name.

They repeat their sounds.

SCENE 11

EXTERIOR: SUBURBAN VILLA; DAY

A villa on the edge of Paris: a clean, white structure. In the garden, a strange scene is taking place. Six or seven people are standing still as statues. One person is crouched on his haunches, wearing earphones, a Nagra on his knees and a microphone directed in different directions.

It looks like a ceremony in which the participants observe a moment of silence in memory of someone.

The silence would be absolute if it weren't for natural noise and the atmosphere: cicadas, roosters, motors, a barge whistle from a nearby canal, a distant train.

The sound man of Tom's small crew, in fact, is recording the sonoral atmosphere. All the others are petrified. The assistant cameraman has his hands in a black bag and is reloading the camera, the scriptgirl is reading *Elle*, the cameraman is looking at the dovecote of a neighboring house.

A taxi door slams. Jeanne arrives, running.

SOUND MAN Stop! *(he looks at her very angrily)* Thanks for the sound! Discretion itself.

The small theater of statues begins moving at once.

Jeanne embraces Tom, who signals to the others to be ready.

JEANNE Hello, everyone. What do you want to start with? The top?

TOM Don't you want to talk first? Just a little?

JEANNE No, today we improvise . . . follow me.

The crew, in fact, is organized to follow Jeanne. She walks briskly toward a corner of the garden. She picks up a bouquet of daisies from a flower bed and walks across the garden. In the shade of a massive hawthorn bush stands a white tombstone. Jeanne bends over to place the daisies at the foot of it.

On the tombstone, an oval photograph—of a magnificent German shepherd. Engraved on the white marble, we read: "Moustapha, Oran 1950–Paris 1958."

JEANNE He was my childhood friend. He used to watch me for hours and hours. Yes, I thought he understood me.

OLDER VOICE (*offscreen*) Dogs are worth more than people. Much more.

The voice comes from a window on the ground floor.

Tom pushes the cameraman to film the face of the old woman who has spoken. We can scarcely see her in the shadows of the kitchen, arms leaning on the window sill.

Her expression is hard.

JEANNE That's Olympia, my nurse.

OLYMPIA Moustapha could always tell the rich from the poor. He never made a mistake. If someone who was well dressed came in, he never moved . . . If a beggar showed up, you should have seen him. What a dog. The colonel, Jeanne's father, trained him to recognize Arabs by their odor.

JEANNE Olympia, open the front door.

OLYMPIA Give me a kiss.

JEANNE Go and open it. Olympia is an anthology of domestic virtues—faithful, admiring, and racist.

The whole group has already reached the entrance.

JEANNE (*offscreen*) After Papa's death we moved to the country house. My childhood was made up of smells. The mold on the walls . . . the closed rooms . . . the smell of marmalade, of clothes being washed. Many children came to play in my jungle. We ran from morning to night . . . Growing old is a crime.

SCENE 12

INTERIOR: VILLA; DAY

A souvenir photograph of an elementary-school class. All the little girls in rows wearing pinafores, with a schoolteacher in front of them. Jeanne is showing off the house where she grew up.

JEANNE That's me. To the right of the teacher, Mademoiselle Sauvage. She was very religious, very severe.

OLYMPIA She was too good. She spoiled you.

The old nanny follows the group, keeping to one side, from time to time grumbling her observations at the top of her voice, offscreen.

JEANNE And that's Christine, my best friend. She married a pharmacist and has a beautiful child. It's a little like a village here. Everybody knows everybody.

OLYMPIA Personally I couldn't live in Paris.

JEANNE We're sheltered here. It's such fun to look at the past.

They are in the small room that belonged to Jeanne as a child. Old toys, children's books, school notebooks. The small crew waits for the director to tell them what to film. Tom leafs through old school notebooks.

TOM Why is it fun? It's you. It's marvelous, it's your childhood, it's everything I've been looking to find . . . And what are you doing there? Who are all these zombies around us? . . . The door! The door! I'm opening the door! I'm opening all the doors!

JEANNE What are you doing?

TOM Setting up a shot . . . There! . . . I found it . . . Reverse gear . . . And what are you doing here? Beat it, scram! Yes. Reverse gear! Understand? Like a car. Put it in reverse. Close your eyes. Back up. Close your eyes. Come forward, backing up. Keep going . . . and find your childhood again.

JEANNE It's Papa . . . There. . . .

TOM You take off . . . and find your childhood again.

JEANNE . . . In full dress uniform.

TOM Don't be afraid. Overcome the obstacles.

JEANNE Papa in Algiers . . .

TOM You are fifteen, fourteen, thirteen, twelve, eleven, ten, nine . . .

JEANNE My favorite street at eight years old. My notebook. My French homework. Theme: "The countryside." Exposition: "The country is the home of the cows. The cow is all dressed in leather. The cow has four sides: front, back, top, and bottom." Isn't that beautiful?

TOM Terrific. What's that?

JEANNE My private diaries are there. Everything's there.

TOM If you don't mind, let's open one.

Jeanne opens a notebook.

JEANNE Here are my cultural sources. The *Grand Larousse*. And I copied it. Menstruation . . . from the latin *menstruus*. Feminine noun. Physiological function consisting of the regular flow of menstrue occurring periodically in a woman from puberty to menopause. Penis. Masculine noun. Organ of copulation, measuring five to forty centimeters . . . This is little Robert! Look, Tom.

Under the photograph is a pastel drawing: a childish drawing, which follows the visual logic and perspective of an eleven-year-old. It shows a boy at the piano.

JEANNE And this drawing. Do you see? I was eleven.

TOM Who is it?

JEANNE My first love, my cousin Paul.

TOM His eyes are closed.

Now the cameraman is filming Jeanne in the living room. She runs her hand over the piano, caressing it.

JEANNE He played the piano magnificently. I remember him seated at the piano, running his slender fingers over the keys. He practiced for hours.

Jeanne tries to stay calm, but clearly she is still troubled. She continues.

JEANNE We used to go to Mass together.

She turns around toward the camera.

JEANNE There are two trees in my garden. A plane tree and a chestnut tree. We sat there each under his tree. My cousin seemed like a saint to me.

Jeanne opens the big door-window. The plane tree and the chestnut are still there, but the childhood sensation is gone. The metal fence around the garden is torn down in places, and a sort of squalid shanty-town is visible a few feet behind it.

JEANNE Aren't they beautiful? For me those trees were a jungle. None of that existed in my time . . . *(to the children)* What are you doing?

Four or five little boys squat in the shade of the two trees, happily relieving themselves. Their expressions alternate between strained grunts and conspiratorial smiles. After a moment's hesitation, they pull up their pants and flee, leaping through gaps in the fence.

But Jeanne is too fast; she catches one by the arm.

FIRST BOY We're shitting.

SECOND BOY Why? Can't you see?

JEANNE Don't you have any place besides my jungle to do that?

She has spoken to him sweetly, but instead of being reassured, the child trembles and struggles to escape. He kicks and curses in a foreign language—because he has seen Olympia emerging from the house in a rage. Jeanne lets him go.

JEANNE Run faster. Beat it.

TOM Shoot! Shoot! Did you get everything?

OLYMPIA If I catch you, I'll hang you. Go shit in your own country, you little bastard.

She throws a rock at him but the boy is already out of range.

OLYMPIA Africa! You can't even live at home any more.

JEANNE (*to Tom*) Did you get it?

TOM All of it.

JEANNE Olympia was magnificent. Now you'll have a precise idea of race relations in the suburbs of Paris.

Tom now hands Jeanne the picture of her father: an officer in uniform with a great sword.

TOM This really is a jungle . . . Tell me about your father.

JEANNE I thought we were finished for the day.

TOM Five minutes.

JEANNE But I'm in a terrible hurry for a business appointment.

TOM Yes, yes . . . well, the colonel?

SCENE 13

INTERIOR: APARTMENT; DAY

The last instants of orgasm, the "little death." Afterward Jeanne slides away from Paul. She turns with her stomach down, and puts her hand on his face. She looks in front of her and talks slowly to Paul, who seems to doze off.

JEANNE The colonel had green eyes and shiny, shiny boots. I worshipped him. He was so handsome in his uniform.

PAUL What a steaming pile of horseshit!

JEANNE What? Don't you dare . . .

PAUL All uniforms are bullshit, everything outside this place is bullshit. Besides, I don't want to hear about your stories, about your past and all that!

He leans on Jeanne and kisses her on the mouth. She is still lost in her memories.

JEANNE At night I could never fall asleep until Mother kissed me. But I always dreamed about my mother's funeral. She's still alive. Papa's the one who died. In Algeria in fifty-eight.

PAUL Or in seventy-eight, or ninety-eight.

JEANNE In fifty-eight! And don't make fun of those things.

PAUL Listen, why don't you stop talking about things that don't matter here? What the hell's the difference?

JEANNE What should I say? What should I do?

PAUL Come on the good ship lollypop.

She sits on the bed, sulking. Then suddenly she has an idea.

JEANNE Why don't you go back to America?

PAUL I don't know. Bad memories I guess.

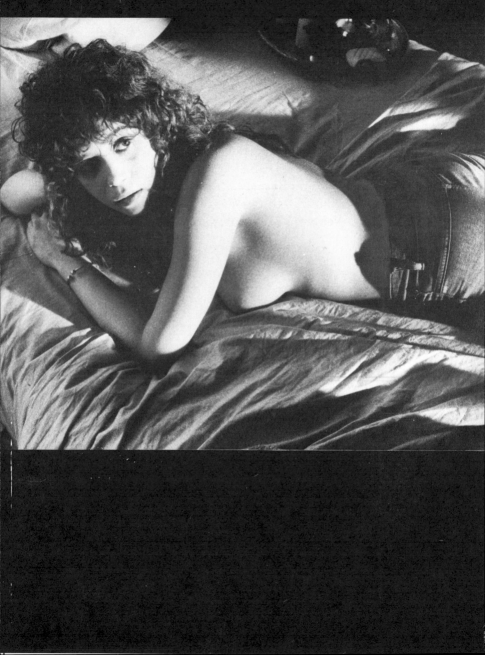

JEANNE (*offscreen*) Bad memories?

PAUL My father was a . . . a drunk, whore-fucker, bar
fighter, super-masculine, and he was tough . . . My
mother was . . . very poetic, also drunk, and my
memories 'bout when I was a kid was of her being
arrested nude. We lived in a small town. Farming
community. We lived on a farm. Well, I'd come
home after school and she'd be gone on a—in jail or
something. I used to have to milk a cow. Every morning and every night. And I liked that, but I remember one time I was all dressed up to go out and
take this girl to a basketball game. And I started to
go out and my father said, "You have to milk the
cow." And I asked him, "Would you please milk it
for me?" And he said, "No, get your ass out there!"
So I went out, and I was in a hurry and didn't have
time to change my shoes, and I had cowshit all over
my shoes, and on the way to the basketball game it
smelled in the car. I don't know . . . Just . . . I—
I can't remember very many good things.

JEANNE (*offscreen*) Not one?

PAUL One. Maybe . . . There was a farmer, a very nice
guy. Old guy, very poor and worked real hard, and
I used to work in a ditch draining land for farming,
and he wore overalls, and he smoked a clay pipe,
and half the time he wouldn't put tobacco in it . . .
he hated work. It was hot and and dirty, and I broke
my back. I'd watch the spit which would run down
the pipe stem and hang on the bowl of the pipe. And
I used to make bets with myself on when it was going
to fall off, and I always lost. Never saw it fall off. I'd

just look around, and it'd be gone, and then the new one would be there. And then we had a beautiful . . . My mother taught me to love nature. I guess that was the most she could do. We had in front of the house . . . we had this big field, meadow . . . it was a mustard field in the summer, and we had a big black dog named Dutchy, and she used to hunt for rabbits in that field. But she couldn't see them, and so she'd have to leap up in this mustard field, look around very quickly to see where the rabbits were, and it was very beautiful even if she never caught the rabbits.

JEANNE You've been had.

PAUL Oh, really?

JEANNE (*ironically*) I don't want to know anything about your past, baby.

PAUL Think I was telling you the truth? Maybe, maybe . . .

JEANNE I'm Little Red Riding Hood and you're the wolf and I say "What strong arms you have!"

PAUL The better to squeeze a fart out of you.

JEANNE What long nails you have.

PAUL The better to scratch your ass with.

JEANNE Oh! What a lot of fur you have.

PAUL The better to let your crabs hide in.

JEANNE Oh! What a long tongue you have.

PAUL The better to . . . stick in your rear, my dear.

JEANNE What's this for?

PAUL That's your happiness and my ha-penis.

JEANNE Peanuts?

PAUL Schlong, Wicknerwurst, cazzo, prick, joint.

> He throws himself on her. Jeanne laughs gaily.

JEANNE It's funny. It's like playing grown-ups when you're little. I feel like a child again here.

PAUL Did you have fun as a kid?

JEANNE It's the most beautiful thing.

PAUL It's the most beautiful thing to be made into a tattle-tale or forced to admire authority, or sell yourself for a piece of candy.

JEANNE I wasn't like that.

PAUL No?

JEANNE I was writing poems, I was drawing castles, big castles, big castles with towers. A lot of towers.

PAUL You never thought about sex?

JEANNE No sex . . . towers.

PAUL You were probably in love with your teacher then.

JEANNE My teacher was a woman.

PAUL Then she was a lesbian.

JEANNE (*screaming*) How did you know?

PAUL That's classical. But anyway . . .

JEANNE My first great love was my cousin Paul.

PAUL I'm going to get a hemorrhoid if you keep telling me names. No names. I don't mind if you tell the truth, but don't give me the names. I can't . . .

JEANNE Sorry . . .

PAUL Well, go on and tell the truth. What else?

JEANNE He was thirteen. Dark, very thin. I can see him. A big nose. A big romance. I fell in love the first time I heard him play the piano.

PAUL You mean when he first got into your knickers.

JEANNE He was a child prodigy. He played with both hands.

PAUL I'll bet he was. Probably getting his kicks.

JEANNE We were dying of the heat.

PAUL Good excuse. And what else?

JEANNE Every afternoon while the grown-ups took their naps . . .

PAUL You started grabbing his joint.

JEANNE You're crazy.

PAUL Well, he touched you.

JEANNE I never let him, never.

PAUL Liar, liar, pants on fire, nose as long as a telephone wire! You mean to tell me that he didn't touch you? Look me straight in the eye and say, "He didn't touch me once." Huh?

JEANNE No, he touched me. But a—the way he did it.

PAUL The way he did it. Okay, what's he do?

JEANNE What we did was much more fun . . . Behind the house there were two trees, a plane tree and a chestnut. I sat under the plane tree, he sat under the chestnut. At a certain signal we'd each begin to masturbate. Whoever came first won. It was perfect. We'd sit there, facing, staring into each other's eyes.

PAUL How old were you when you came for the first time?

JEANNE The first time? I was late for school. I began running downhill. Suddenly I felt a strong sensation here. I came as I ran . . . then I ran faster and faster and the more I ran . . . the more I came. Two days later I tried running again, but . . . no dice! . . . Why don't you listen to me? You know, it seems to me I'm talking to the wall. Your solitude weighs on me, you know. It isn't indulgent or generous. You're an egoist . . . I can be by myself too, you know.

The doorbell rings. Jeanne is surprised, as if that sound was impossible in this place. Paul goes to the door. He is about to open it.

VOICE (*offscreen*) The Bible complete . . . unique edition . . . without notes . . . without cuts . . .

Jeanne has leaped to stop Paul. The doorbell rings again.
Paul stretches his hand toward the doorknob. Jeanne bites it.

PAUL Aie . . .

JEANNE Did we make a pact—yes or no? Nobody must see us together. You could kill me and no one would know, not even this Bible freak.

Paul puts his hands around her neck and playfully begins to squeeze her throat.

JEANNE (*in a low voice, playfully*) Help!

VOICE (*offscreen*) The true Bible . . . don't close your door to eternity.

Paul turns her around and, pressed against her back, he clasps one hand over her mouth. With the

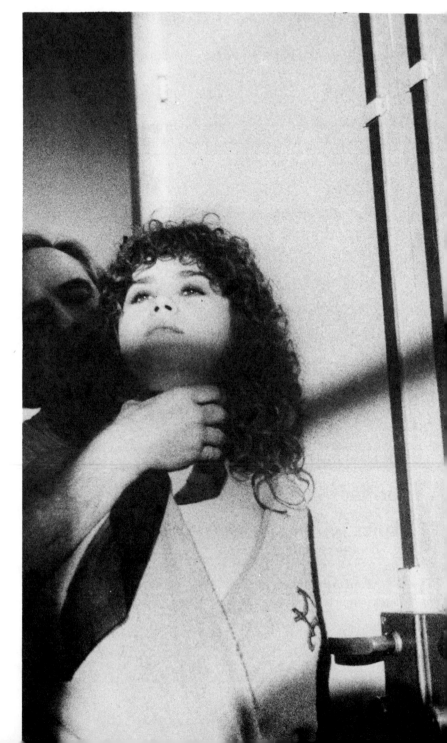

other, he continues to clasp her throat. He whispers in her ear.

PAUL Not him . . . or the concierge . . . who's half blind, anyway.

JEANNE You don't even have a motive . . . The perfect crime . . . in fact . . . It's stupid. Let me go . . . I don't feel like it anymore.

Paul lets her go. She walks away while he continues to listen, with his ear against the door. We hear Jeanne open the bathroom door.

VOICE (*offscreen*) Someone is in there! Open the door to the Jehovah's Witness.

The Bible man knocks insistently at the door. Paul waits for Jeanne to go into the bathroom.

Paul opens the front door abruptly. Bent in half, his eyes at the keyhole, the "Bible salesman" jumps back, caught in the act of peeping. He is tall, very thin, hairless, a kind of worm. Now he faces a completely nude Paul, who barks at him.

PAUL Stop bugging us! Biblical pig! Get lost! Go!

The salesman runs down the stairs.

SCENE 14

Still another door that opens abruptly. Paul appears. This is a hotel room like the others but . . . very different. There are flowers everywhere. Too many flowers. Even the sink is filled with them, a great bunch of white carnations waiting for a vase. Raymond, the concierge of the hotel, appears behind Paul.

RAYMOND It looks good, doesn't it, boss?

In the room the two beds have been put together. The empty bed is surrounded by flowers, wreaths and garlands. It is obviously waiting for the corpse of Rosa. In some other room someone is tuning an instrument. We hear soft pieces of music, loud pieces of music, and then long silences. It must be a tenor saxophone.

PAUL Only Rosa is missing.

RAYMOND Your mother-in-law needed something to do.

Raymond moves a wreath as he mumbles to himself.

RAYMOND This is a nice, quiet room. Inside window, no noise. Except for that closet . . . Madame Rosa wanted to sell it. That closet is a nest of worms.

He has pushed the bed against the wall, leaving the

other in the middle of the room. He goes quietly to the closet and puts his ear against it, looking at Paul for agreement.

RAYMOND You can hear them in the wood . . . sss . . . sss . . . I always put South Americans in this room.

PAUL South Americans?

RAYMOND Of course. South Americans never leave tips. *"No tengo dinero,"* they always say. *"Mañana, mañana."*

Paul leaves the room with Raymond, who closes the door.

RAYMOND It's better to lock it. You never know, if a client comes in the middle of the night . . .

PAUL (*joking unpleasantly*) "We're full up, Mister. Only the funeral parlor's free."

They walk down the hall.

RAYMOND It does you good to laugh a little. That's what Madame Rosa always said.

SCENE 15
INTERIOR: HALL; NIGHT

They arrive in the hall. A woman is leaning on the

desk, bent over the register. She jumps back when she sees them. Very made-up, of uncertain age, red-blond hair. Raymond closes the register ostentatiously.

Paul goes into a neighboring room. We can hear the woman speak.

MISS BLANDISH (*offscreen*) No interesting new faces today?

Paul makes coffee. His movements are precise. Evidently he is used to making it.

MISS BLANDISH Paul! Want to bet the races with me?

Miss Blandish is in the entrance of the room.

PAUL The races? Why not? Want some coffee?

MISS BLANDISH Not now. Poor Rosa and I knew a jockey who used to give us tips.

PAUL Rosa never told me. Did you win?

MISS BLANDISH Never. But it was a distraction, and then Rosa loved horses so much. We were planning to buy one together.

PAUL She didn't know anything about them.

Miss Blandish stops talking and looks curiously at a man coming down the stairs. His bare legs are visible under his coat, which he wears as a robe on his nude body. He addresses Raymond.

MARLOWE (*American accent*) Didn't anybody call for me?

RAYMOND No one.

The man's eyes look toward the door. Miss Blandish butts into the conversation.

MISS BLANDISH Hello, Mister Marlowe . . . How are you?

The man doesn't seem to recognize her. Then, after an instant, he replies in a low voice.

MARLOWE Terrific, Miss Blandish. Terrific.

He goes back up the stairs. As soon as he disappears, she imitates his voice and his sunken cheeks.

MISS BLANDISH Terrific, Miss Blandish. Terrific.

She turns back to Paul, resuming their conversation.

MISS BLANDISH What are you talking about? She knew a lot about horses. The circus people taught her to ride.

Paul is pouring himself a cup of coffee, and looks at her strangely, but Miss Blandish's attention wanders again. A young man with short hair enters the hotel and approaches Raymond. The collar of his coat is up. He speaks so softly that Miss Blandish can't hear what he's said. So she turns back to Paul.

MISS BLANDISH Yes, yes . . . Rosa ran away when she was thirteen, to join an Italian circus. Funny she never told you about it.

Raymond appears in the doorway.

RAYMOND There's a guy out front . . . only speaks English. All I got is that he doesn't have any papers.

PAUL Go to sleep, Raymond. I'll take care of it.

RAYMOND Thanks, boss.

Miss Blandish observes the scene. Raymond takes his raincoat off a hook, and his briefcase. The young man is sitting and waiting. Paul finishes his coffee, and Raymond comes to say good-bye before leaving.

RAYMOND No passport. No baggage. No money either, if you ask me. Good night, boss.

PAUL Good night, Raymond.

MISS BLANDISH Good night, Raymond.

Raymond exits. Paul approaches the young man, but before speaking to him glances pointedly at Miss Blandish. She understands, and goes toward the stairs, murmuring.

MISS BLANDISH Why did she do that . . . Sunday was the Grand Prix at Auteuil. What an idea—to die.

She disappears up the stairs. Paul scrutinizes the

young man, who holds his coat by the collar. He carries only a small package under one arm.

PAUL Where are you coming from?

YOUNG MAN Düsseldorf . . . Winter's very long there.

PAUL So I've heard. You're the third one this winter.

YOUNG MAN About the passport . . . I'll have one in a couple of days.

Paul takes a key off the board.

PAUL Top floor.

YOUNG MAN About the money . . . I don't know when I'll be able to pay you.

Paul goes toward the kitchen. Before entering it, he turns around.

PAUL Last door.

The young man starts up the stairs.
The last floor. The young man walks down the hall. A door opens. Marlowe in his raincoat watches him pass. It is not the person he is waiting for. He lets him go by, then sits on the first step of the staircase and waits.
The last door. The young man enters, and locks the door behind him. He rips his package open. It contains a pair of bluejeans, a shirt, and a pullover sweater. At the same time, he takes off his coat. He is wearing the

uniform of a U.S. soldier. He undresses with abrupt gestures and rolls his uniform into a ball, looking for a place to hide it. Far away, we hear the saxophone. It has finally found its melody, and repeats it obsessively. Marlowe crouches on the stairs.

Downstairs, Paul also listens to the distant music that comes from the bowels of his hotel. Sitting in the little room, he surveys the objects that surround him. It is his last tie with Rosa. He closes his eyes.

SCENE 16

INTERIOR: HOTEL; NIGHT

How long did Paul keep his eyes closed? Ten seconds? Two hours? It's difficult to say.

The sound of the saxophone grows louder and softer with the regularity of a wave.

Sitting beside him, Rosa's mother looks at him. She is wearing a bathrobe and a shawl.

MOTHER I can't sleep. That music . . .

Paul talks without looking at her.

PAUL I came to this hotel to spend the night. I stayed five years.

MOTHER When we had this hotel, Papa and me, people came here to sleep.

PAUL Now there's everything. You can hide here, take drugs here, play music. Don't touch me.

The mother-in-law puts her hand gently on Paul's shoulder.

MOTHER You're not alone, Paul. I'm here.

Paul bites her hand.

MOTHER You're crazy. I'm beginning to understand.

PAUL Rosa was a lot like you. People must have told you often . . . Isn't that right, Mother?

The shadow of a smile is on her lips.

MOTHER Up until ten years ago they were still saying it—two sisters . . .

PAUL It's not true at all. Rosa was very different from you.

MOTHER That music . . . that music . . . I can't stand it.

PAUL Do you want me to make them stop.

He gets up and raises a hand suddenly.

PAUL I'll make them shut up.

He touches a fuse box and pulls a lever down. Suddenly it is pitch black. It is the fuse box for the entire hotel.

MOTHER Paul, what are you doing?

The silence is profound. Even the saxophone is mute.

PAUL They've stopped. What's the matter, Mother, you upset? Don't be upset. Nothing to be upset about.

In the dark Paul and his mother-in-law move, barely lit by reflections from the street. They go to the staircase. We hear a door open, then others, then worried voices in the dark, inquiring what is happening in French, in English, in Italian. Someone strikes a match; the clients quiet down. We see the stairwell full of silhouettes snatched out of the still of the night. The match burns out. Imprecations. Someone calls Paul.

PAUL You know, it takes so little to make them afraid. Do you want me to tell you what they're afraid of. They're afraid of the dark, imagine that.

MOTHER Paul . . . put the lights on.

PAUL Come on, Mother. I want you to meet my friends. I think you ought to meet the clients of the hotel. Hey folks, I'd like you to say hello to Mom. Mom, this is Mr. Juice head junky here. He's our connection Mom. And Mr. Saxophone here . . . And right here is the beautiful Best Blow Job of 1933. She's still making a few points when she takes her teeth out.

MOTHER The lights, Paul.

PAUL Don't you want to say hello? Mom! This is Mom.

MOTHER The lights. Light the lights.

PAUL Oh, are you afraid of the dark, Mom? She's afraid of the dark. Aw, well, poor thing. All right, sweetheart. I'll take care of you. Don't worry about it. I'll give you a little light. I'll give you a little light. Don't worry about a thing.

She leans on the desk. After a moment the lights come back on. There is an unknown man in the entrance. He looks at her without speaking. He is wearing a coat and muffler. He must have come in while it was dark. They look like two statues. After a second he takes his hat off and greets her gently.

MARCEL Good evening, Ma'am.

The hotel guests have calmed down, the doors are closed again. Paul comes out of the room with a coffee cup in his hand and sees the man, who is taking down a key by himself. He has a package of newspapers under his arm.

MARCEL Good night, Paul.

PAUL Good night, Marcel.

Marcel starts up the stairs. The mother-in-law follows him with her eyes.

MOTHER Who is that?

PAUL Do you like him? He was Rosa's lover.

SCENE 17

INTERIOR: APARTMENT; DAY

Jeanne is in the bathroom. Her make-up is all smeared. Her hair is a mess.

JEANNE What am I doing in this apartment with you?

PAUL Let's say we're just taking a flying fuck at a rolling doughnut.

JEANNE So you think I'm a whore.

PAUL No. You're just a dear old-fashioned girl trying to get along.

Paul goes away. Jeanne is alone.

JEANNE I prefer to be a whore.

She sees Paul's jacket on the clothes rack. She begins her inquiry modestly. She scrutinizes the label . . . an unknown shop, an address on the boulevards. Then she screws up her courage and rifles the pockets on both sides. Some loose change, a used subway ticket, a broken cigarette. Jeanne pursues her investigation in the breast pocket. She finds a crumpled wad of hundred-franc notes. Nothing else. No papers. No identification.

Jeanne puts the jacket back just in time, an instant before Paul comes into the room.

In the ancient bathroom are two sinks, adjoining, each with its own mirror. Jeanne occupies one, her cosmetics arranged on the white porcelain. She puts on her make-up.

PAUL Why were you going through my pockets?

JEANNE To find out who you are.

PAUL Well, if you look real close, you'll see me hiding behind my zipper.

He starts lathering up his face.

JEANNE We know he buys clothes in some big store. It's not much, but it's a beginning.

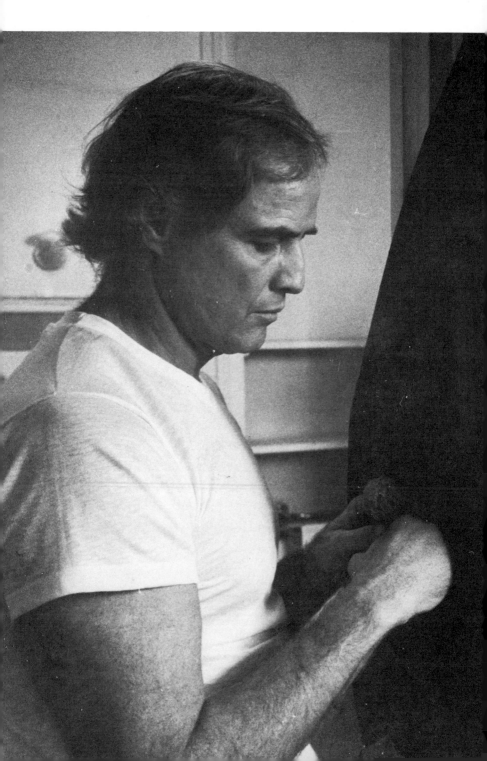

She has spoken without looking at him. He doesn't look at her either. They seem to be interested in only mascara and shaving cream. Paul begins to shave.

PAUL That's not a beginning, that's a finish.

JEANNE Let's forget it. How old are you?

PAUL I'll be ninety-three this weekend.

JEANNE That's much better. Oh, you don't look it. Have you been in college?

PAUL Yeah, I went to the University of Congo, studied whale fucking.

JEANNE Barbers don't usually go to university.

PAUL Are you telling me that I—that I look like a barber?

JEANNE No, but that's a razor's barber.

PAUL That's a barber's razor.

JEANNE A barber's razor, yes.

PAUL Or a madman's.

Jeanne turns around abruptly. There's something strange and fascinating: She has made-up only half of her face; the other half is completely clean.

JEANNE So you want to cut me up?

Paul approaches Jeanne and turns her face from side to side, stroking it lightly with the blunt side of the razor.

PAUL That would be like writing my name on your face.

JEANNE Like they do the slaves?

PAUL Slaves are branded on the ass, and I want you free.

JEANNE Free, I'm not free.

PAUL You are free to come fucking with me.

JEANNE Free, shit! I come running here . . . to fuck, yes . . . You want to know why you don't want to know anything about me? Because you hate women! What have they ever done to you?

PAUL Either they always pretend to know who I am, or they pretend that I don't know who they are, and that's very boring.

JEANNE I'm not afraid to say who I am. I'm twenty years old and . . .

PAUL Jesus Christ! Don't wear out your brain! Shut up. Get it? I know it's tough, but you're going to have to bear it.

The catch in his voice silences Jeanne.

PAUL The only truth is . . .

Then, after a glance at her, his voice softens.

PAUL . . . These twin sinks are a beautiful invention. They're rare, you don't find them anymore. They've been devised so we can stay together even after we make love . . . so our happiness gets longer . . . I think I'm happy with you.

He kisses her gently on the cheek, leaving on her nose a white smear of shaving cream. He goes out of the bathroom.

A few minutes have gone by. Jeanne is in the bathroom, drying her hair with a towel. With her face hidden she reaches for the door, opens it, and yells.

JEANNE I'm finished. Shall we go together?

No answer. She wraps herself in a bathtowel.

JEANNE Hey, do you hear me?

Nothing. She walks through the apartment. Her clothes are on the floor. Paul's clothes have disappeared. She walks toward the hall, and arrives there just as Paul is going out, slamming the door in her face.

JEANNE Bastard . . . Pig . . . Not even good-bye.

She goes to the telephone and dials a number.

TOM (*offscreen*) Hello.

Jeanne doesn't reply, waiting for Tom to lose his temper.

TOM (*offscreen*) Hello . . . who is it? . . . Hello . . . who's there? Shit!

JEANNE Just as I thought. You get vulgar right away. Listen . . . something awful's happened. I'm in Passy . . . No, I don't have time to explain . . . Come get me. I have to talk to you immediately. It's very important.

Suddenly her expression changes . . . she is not listening anymore. Tom is questioning her.

TOM In Passy? Whereabouts?

She isn't listening. She leaves the receiver on the floor with one hand while with the other she picks up a shoe and turns around slowly toward the open window.

On the sill the black cat is staring at her. Jeanne remembers the telephone and mumbles.

JEANNE At the subway stop.

Tiptoeing, she approaches the cat with her shoe above her head, ready to throw it at the animal. The cat goes toward the front door. Violently Jeanne hurls her shoe at it. The shoe bounces off the door.

SCENE 18

EXTERIOR: PASSY SUBWAY STATION ABOVE
RUE JULES VERNE; NIGHT

The metro arrives, stopping suddenly. Tom gets off and looks for Jeanne. The other passengers go off quickly toward the exit. The platform is now practically deserted. Tom goes over to the railing. He looks down, toward the bridge, where rue Jules Verne is visible in the quiet night. He looks up to the buildings, next to the windows of Paul's apartment. But for Tom these places have no meaning. The train starts again behind him.

JEANNE (*offscreen*) Tom!

She is calling from the platform on the other side of the tracks.

TOM What are you doing there?

JEANNE I have to talk to you.

Tom starts toward the other platform, but Jeanne's voice stops him.

JEANNE Don't come over. Stay there.

Tom makes a strange face—he is ready to burst, but finally his anger subsides. He starts to whistle to calm his nerves, and paces on the platform. Jeanne follows him on the parallel platform. Suddenly he says:

TOM Why wouldn't you tell me over the telephone? What's the matter?

JEANNE You must find somebody else.

Tom stops whistling. Without looking at her he asks:

TOM For what?

JEANNE For your film.

TOM Why?

JEANNE Because!

She is getting angry. Her voice gets louder.

JEANNE Because you're taking advantage of me, because you force me to do things I've never done before, because you take up my time . . . and because of the kind of things you make me do . . . Anything that comes into your head. The film is finished, understand?

The last few words are lost in the roar of a subway entering the station. Jeanne sees Tom, who is yelling something at her, but the subway car covers him up. The subway leaves, uncovering the opposite platform as it goes. Jeanne yells.

JEANNE (*screaming*) I'm tired of being raped!

But there's nobody opposite her. Tom has disap-

TRÈS CONCENTRÉ
VIGOR
NETTOYANT
INDUSTRIEL
VIGOR
La puissance
d'un nettoyant industriel
au service de vos sols

peared. She goes toward the exit. She stops. He is a few steps away. He looks at her attentively for an instant, without saying a word, while going around her at the same time.

Tom slaps her, hard. She slaps him back before he's had time to withdraw his hand. A moment passes, they regard each other aggressively, each rubbing his cheek. Then they throw themselves at each other. Fist-fighting, kicking, biting.

It looks like the fight of two adolescents. Another train arrives and hides them from us. When the platform empties again, we have the impression they are embracing—an impression that lasts for one moment only, because another train covers them up. It really looked like they were kissing each other.

SCENE 19

INTERIOR: MARCEL'S ROOM, HOTEL; NIGHT

The red shadow of Paul's robe. A newspaper page. Long scissors cut out a photograph with its caption. Someone knocks at the door.

MARCEL Come in.

Paul comes in. Marcel, sitting, with the scissors, barely looks at him.

PAUL You wanted to talk to me? Go ahead, but I didn't come here to cry with you.

MARCEL I hope it won't bother you if I keep working. It helps me a great deal.

Only now does Paul notice that Marcel is wearing an identical robe. He is about to mention it, but changes his mind. The other man, with spectacles balanced on the end of his nose, continues.

MARCEL It helps me a great deal; after what happened.

While he is saying this, with a side glance over his spectacles he has observed Paul's curiosity about the robe.

MARCEL The same color. The same pattern. If you only knew how many things we have in common.

More annoyed than embarrassed, Paul goes over to Marcel's table and picks up one of the clippings, if only to have something to do.

PAUL You can't tell me anything that I don't know already. I've always wondered, Marcel, you keep these press clippings . . . Is it your work or is it a hobby?

MARCEL Hobby? I don't care for that word. Let's say, it helps me out at the end of the month. I do it for an agency. It's a job that makes you read. Very instructive. Be sincere. Didn't you know we had identical bathrobes? We have lots of things in common. And I like it. I wanted to tell you before that perhaps you didn't know about the robe. And maybe you don't know about so many little things more. ,

PAUL I know everything. Rosa told me everything. If you only know how many times we talked about you. I don't think there are many marriages like that . . . I'm thirsty.

He goes toward the door.

PAUL You want a little bourbon?

MARCEL Wait!

He leans over and takes a bottle of bourbon and two glasses out of the night table.

MARCEL Here you are.

This time Paul is sincerely surprised, and doesn't attempt to hide it.

PAUL Is that a present from Rosa too?

He sits on the bed.

MARCEL Personally, I don't like bourbon. But Rosa always wanted me to have a bottle in the night table. That's the question I've been asking myself. If . . . with these details . . . unimportant things . . . we could think back, understand together . . . It's been almost a year that Rosa and I . . . not passionately but regularly . . . I thought I knew her as is possible one can know . . .

LT-1-6

PAUL One's mistress.

MARCEL For example, some time ago something happened which I haven't been able to explain . . . You see the wall over there?

He indicates a corner near the ceiling, where the wallpaper has obviously been torn.

MARCEL She climbed on the chair and tried to tear the paper with her bare hands. I stopped her because she was breaking all her nails.

He looks at Paul, waiting for an explanation. None comes.

MARCEL She was so violent about it, so strange. I'd never seen her like that.

Paul rises and looks around him, as if searching for other signs. He also opens the bathroom door.

PAUL Our room is painted white. Rosa wanted it to be different from the other rooms. To have the feeling of a normal home. Here . . . it had to change too . . . She started with the wallpaper.

There's a note of bitterness in Marcel's voice now.

MARCEL Maybe I was never anything more than a replacement.

Marcel stands up suddenly, letting his clippings and

his scissors fall. He presses the thumb of his left hand
in the right hand.

MARCEL Shit! That's the first time in ten years . . .

A rivulet of red blood trickles out of his cut hand
and quickly spreads over the back of it. Paul takes him
over to the sink and puts his hand under running water.
A lot of blood but not a serious cut, only a scratch.

MARCEL She bathed and dressed, fixed her hair and
climbed the stairs. She came here as if she were going
downtown . . . I can't stand physical pain.

Paul goes back into the room to pick up the bourbon bottle. With one hand he takes Marcel's wrist and
with the other pours the alcohol over the cut, after taking the cork out with his teeth. Marcel looks away.

PAUL We always told each other everything. From the
beginning . . . No secrets, no lies . . . even adultery
. . . adultery became part . . . part of our marriage.

MARCEL It burns!

Paul continues to pour out the bourbon without
stopping.

PAUL But this was not my agreement with Rosa. Here
Rosa constructs a second husband . . . dresses him
like the first . . .

MARCEL Makes him drink the same rotgut . . .

PAUL You were lucky enough . . . You must have been a good-looking man twenty years ago.

MARCEL Not as much as you.

PAUL You have all your hair.

MARCEL I have to cut it often. And wash it.

PAUL Do you have massages?

MARCEL Yes. Massages also.

PAUL You're in good shape. What do you do for—for the belly?

MARCEL The belly?

PAUL That's my problem.

MARCEL Here . . . I have a secret.

PAUL What?

MARCEL Thinking of leaving? I saw your suitcase . . . eh . . . America . . . Why did she betray you with me?

PAUL You don't think Rosa killed herself? It's difficult for me too, to believe it.

MARCEL Here's my secret. Thirty times, every morning.

Marcel chins himself.

PAUL I was looking for a letter from Rosa. But the letter is you . . .

The bottle is now empty. Paul doesn't seem to have noticed it. He continues to hold Marcel's wrist in his hand, tighter and tighter. Marcel is not afraid or worried any more.

MARCEL Paul, let go of my wrist, you're hurting me. Let go, Paul!

Paul lets go. On the white porcelain, in a glass is Marcel's razor. That one is also a straight razor.
Paul goes quickly toward the door.

PAUL Really, Marcel, I wonder what she ever saw in you.

SCENE 20

Interior: Elevator, Rue Jules Verne; Day

Jeanne is in the elevator, which is ascending. She holds a red record-player case in her hand. She opens the door with her key, disappears inside the apartment, and closes the door.

SCENE 21

Seen from the entrance, the apartment looks empty. The girl puts the case down.

JEANNE Are you there?

No answer. She opens a closet and puts the red-cased record player inside.

She is ready to leave again when she sees the reflection of something in a mirror. She approaches softly. This time it isn't the black cat. It's Paul, sitting cross-legged on the floor. In front of him there is a plate with bread, cheese, a knife.

JEANNE Hi monster. Something wrong?

PAUL There's butter in the kitchen.

JEANNE So, you're here. Why didn't you answer?

PAUL Go get the butter.

JEANNE I'm in a hurry. I have a taxi waiting downstairs.

Jeanne is so dumbfounded that she obeys without thinking. She returns with the butter and throws it onto his plate. Paul doesn't react. Exasperated, she sits in front of him with an air of defiance.

JEANNE It makes me crazy that you're so damned sure I'll come back.

Paul smiles at her, buttering his bread.

JEANNE What do you think? Because you think an American sitting on the floor in an empty apartment eating cheese is interesting?

He says nothing. She drums her fingernails irritably on the parquet floor.

JEANNE There's something underneath. I can feel it.

She seems to be talking about the situation. Instead, she searches the cracks in the discolored parquet with her fingers. She hits the floor. The sound is hollow, like a tambourine. With her index finger she brings out an almost invisible fault that follows the lines of the parquet.

JEANNE Do you hear? It's hollow.

Paul joins her, crawling on all fours. He hits the floor near Jeanne's fingers twice with his fist.

PAUL That's a hiding place.

He manages to lift a piece of the floor with his finger. A tiny trap door, the size of a brick, appears on the floor.

JEANNE Don't open it!

PAUL Why not?

JEANNE I don't know. Don't open it.

PAUL What about that, can I open that? . . . Wait a minute. Maybe there's jewels in it. Maybe there's gold. You afraid? You're always afraid.

Paul's hand caresses the trap door. All at once he seems about to get it opened. Jeanne's hand seizes his fist, her nails embedded in his skin.

JEANNE No. But maybe there's some family secrets inside.

PAUL Family secrets? I'll tell you about family secrets.

Paul rolls on top of her, pinning her arms to the floor. Using the butter as a lubricant, he enters her from behind.

JEANNE What are you doing?

PAUL I'm going to tell you about the family. That holy institution, meant to breed virtue into savages. I want you to repeat it after me.

JEANNE No and no!

PAUL Repeat it!

His fists dig into her, hurting her.

PAUL Holy family. Come on, say it. Go on! Holy family, the church of good citizens.

JEANNE Church . . . Good citizens. (*cries*)

Paul loosens his hold.

PAUL Say it. The children are tortured until they tell their first lie.

JEANNE The children . . .

PAUL Where the will is broken by repression.

JEANNE Where the will is broken . . . repression. (*sobs*)

PAUL Where freedom is assassinated.

JEANNE Freedom is . . . (*sobs*)

PAUL Is assassinated . . . Freedom is assassinated by egotism . . . family.

JEANNE . . . family.

PAUL You fucking—fucking family. (*gasps*) You fucking family. Oh God, Jesus.

A moment passes. They are silent. Jeanne calms down. She goes to plug the record player into the socket, and jumps at the shock she receives.

JEANNE Shit. Hey, you! Yes, you.

PAUL Yeah?

JEANNE I've got a surprise for you.

PAUL What?

JEANNE I've got a surprise for you.

PAUL That's good. I like surprises. What is it?

JEANNE Music. But I don't know how to work it.

He bends over the phonograph. He takes the plug and moves toward the socket. He plugs it into the socket, and also receives the shock.

PAUL You enjoy that?

SCENE 22
EXTERIOR: BARGE; DAY

The boat is called *L'Atalante*. It is anchored with long metal cables. It has been there for a long time. It has been turned into a dancing hall and is ready to go to demolition. Jeanne is working. She is bargaining with the old owner (an old man with a tattooed chest, identical to Michel Simon's. Maybe it is he) about a group of objects very typically "art deco" lamps, various decorations, etc.

Now the small crew is reunited on the prow, beneath a kind of dilapidated pergola or hanging bower. Tom interviews Jeanne. The old man had started to say, "I'm not going to sell anything" but the girl's charm fascinates him and he then lets go, piece by piece, many objects. The old captain has put a 78-rpm record on his old phonograph: "Parlami d'amore Mariu."

TOM What is your profession?

JEANNE I'm a busybody.

TOM I thought you were an antique dealer.

JEANNE I dig things up. I look around. I've told you: I'm a busybody.

TOM What kind of things?

JEANNE Everything from eighteen eighty to nineteen thirty-five.

TOM Why just those years.

JEANNE Because, in antiques, those years were revolutionary.

TOM I don't understand. Repeat, please. What kind of years were they?

JEANNE Revolutionary. Yes, Art Nouveau is revolutionary in comparison with the rest of the nineteenth century and the Victorian era. Compared with bric-a-brac and bad taste.

TOM Bad taste? Taste? What's that? And how can you feel revolutionary about collecting old things that once were revolutionary?

JEANNE Do you want a fight?

TOM Okay, okay . . . Where do you find these . . . revolutionary objects?

JEANNE At auctions, at different markets, in the country, in private homes . . .

TOM You go into people's homes? What kind of people?

JEANNE Old people . . . or else, their sons, nephews, grandchildren. They wait for the old folks to die. And then they sell it all, as fast as they can.

TOM Isn't that a little morbid? The smell of old things. The remains of the dead?

JEANNE No, it's exciting. The way I operate, the past is exciting. It's a find . . . an object with a history. Listen, once I found the alarm clock of the executioner of Paris.

TOM That's disgusting. You'd like to sleep with the hangman's alarm clock next to your bed? I don't have to think twice to choose between an antique house and a clean, clear room. You'll see . . . few pieces of furniture . . . glass and chrome . . . light even in the objects, everything new . . . new things. You are like a film with a technical error: The sound doesn't synchronize with the visual. We listen to you talking of old, dusty things while we see your clean healthy, modern appearance.

JEANNE It's a way of refusing the present, a way of . . . I'm having a dress made like the one my mother wore in a picture of nineteen forty-six. How beautiful she was, and young, with those square shoulders.

TOM Why this fascination with the forties?

JEANNE Because it's easier to love something that doesn't affect us too directly . . . something which keeps a certain distance . . . Like you with your camera . . .

TOM A distance . . . I'll see.

Suddenly he turns to the cameraman.

TOM Give me the camera, Alain, I'll go on from here . . .

Everyone goes except the scriptgirl.

TOM Beat it!

The scriptgirl goes, reluctantly. Finally they are alone.

TOM Sit down.

JEANNE What shall I say?

TOM I'll ask you questions. Know why I sent everyone away?

JEANNE Because you are angry or want to talk alone with me.

TOM And why?

JEANNE Because you have something important to tell me.

TOM It's something very important.

JEANNE Happy or sad?

TOM It's a secret.

JEANNE Then it's happy. What kind of secret?

TOM A secret between a man and a woman.

JEANNE Dirt or love?

TOM Love. And it's not everything.

JEANNE A love secret that isn't everything? What is it?

TOM That in a week I'm marrying you.

JEANNE Oh, my God!

TOM That is if you accept.

JEANNE And you . . .

TOM I've decided. Everything's ready . . .

JEANNE Tom, everything is so strange. It seems impossible to me.

TOM The picture is a little out of focus, but emotion makes my hands tremble . . . You haven't answered yet.

JEANNE Because I don't know what is going on anymore.

TOM Well? Yes or no?

JEANNE Stop shooting. I'm supposed to marry you, not the camera.

Tom exuberantly throws a life preserver into the water. It sinks.

SCENE 23

INTERIOR: JEANNE'S APARTMENT; DAY

The apartment in which Jeanne lives with her mother is a kingdom of anonymous bourgeois comfort and decorations. Her mother resembles the apartment.

Jeanne is looking at her mother, who is busy. Jeanne's mother carries several uniforms and objects from the closet to the bed. She is holding a pair of boots.

JEANNE'S MOTHER Tell me . . . What do you think, shall I send them?

JEANNE Olympia will be happy. I went there yesterday with Tom. She's preparing a family museum.

JEANNE'S MOTHER Papa's boots, no. I'll keep them. They give me strange shivers when I touch them.

Jeanne dons the kepi at a rakish angle. She caresses the material of the uniform.

JEANNE'S MOTHER Uniforms . . . All those military things which never age.

She has picked up a shiny holster now, with a regulation military pistol inside.

JEANNE It used to seem so heavy when I was little . . . and Papa was teaching me to shoot it. Why don't you send it? What are you going to do with a gun?

Her mother is busy packing things in two large suitcases.

JEANNE'S MOTHER In any respectable household, a firearm is always useful.

Jeanne rummages in a box full of old papers, a passport.

JEANNE You don't even know how to hold it.

JEANNE'S MOTHER The important thing is to have it. It has its own effect.

Jeanne is attracted by a red leather wallet. She rolls onto her stomach in order to escape her mother's eyes and extracts the Colonel's old identity card. Under the card, very well hidden, is a small yellow photograph of a young girl who smiles, happily, with her breasts in the air.

Jeanne hides the wallet in her purse, then turns suddenly back to her mother.

JEANNE You've saved everything of Papa's. And her? Who is she? His orderly?

Curious, the mother takes the photograph. She is a little embarrassed, but immediately finds a justification.

JEANNE'S MOTHER Fine example of a Berber. A hardy race. I tried to keep several in the house. But they make terrible domestics . . . I'm glad I decided to send all that to the country house . . . Things keep piling up.

Jeanne gives her a kiss.

JEANNE Soon, you'll have all the room you want. I've got to go. I haven't finished working. I just stopped by to tell you . . .

She breaks out of her mother's embrace and dashes out. Her mother follows her as far as the door.

JEANNE'S MOTHER Tell me what?

JEANNE Nothing. Madame, the Colonel's lady, I announce . . .

JEANNE'S MOTHER What?

JEANNE That in these solemn days . . .

JEANNE'S MOTHER What solemn days?

But Jeanne is already running down the stairs. Just before she disappears she calls out.

JEANNE I'm getting married . . . I'm getting married in a week.

SCENE 24

INTERIOR: FLEA MARKET, BRIDAL SHOP; DAY

The shop is so small that the camera is placed on the sidewalk.
The cameraman is filming.
Jeanne is half hidden by two salesgirls. Standing up and crouched, they are trying a dress on her, adjusting it to her size with pins and ribbons.

TOM How do you see marriage?

JEANNE I see it . . . all the time.

TOM What's that—all the time?

JEANNE Yes, on walls, all over buildings . . . Does that surprise you?

TOM On walls, buildings?

JEANNE Of course, on billboards. What is advertising talking about? What is it selling?

TOM Well . . . cars, cigarettes, canned meat.

JEANNE Wrong. The subject of advertising is the young couple. Before marriage, without children, and the same couple after marriage and with children. In short, marriage.

TOM Deep down, I suppose that's true.

JEANNE No, it's not true. But it might as well be. The perfect marriage—happy, successful, ideal—can no longer be found between the walls of a church. That kind of marriage is based on endless obstacles which the couple has to overcome. That way, you have a husband loaded with responsibility and a nagging wife. In publicity, it's just the opposite. There, marriage smiles.

TOM Smiles . . . in advertisements?

JEANNE Sure. But in the end, I say, why not? Why not take advertising's marriage seriously? Marriage that's . . . pop.

TOM There's the formula. For youth that's pop, a pop marriage. But suppose that a pop marriage isn't working. What do you do?

JEANNE Marriage is a product, a machine. If it isn't working, you have to repair it, like you repair a car. A couple are two workers in overalls who bend over a motor and fix it.

TOM What happens to a pop marriage if there's adultery, for instance?

JEANNE All right, in case of adultery . . . instead of two workers . . . there are three . . . or four.

TOM What about children?

JEANNE Oh, them. Before you created them. Now you produce them.

TOM What's the difference?

JEANNE When marriage and love were synonymous, you created them. Now, just the opposite. Marriage is a product which produces children. You make a machine which produces a series of little machines. Little pop machines.

TOM Is love pop too?

JEANNE No, not that.

TOM Then, what is it?

JEANNE The workers go to a secret apartment . . . They take off their overalls, turn back into men and women, and make love.

TOM But that's just adultery, from five to seven. The same old stuff.

JEANNE Love and adultery are the same thing. If you don't cheat. That is part of the whole thing.

TOM And this?

JEANNE This is unforeseen . . . This is *the* unforeseen.

TOM You disappoint me: I thought that the unforeseen . . . would have been foreseen.

JEANNE Love catches us by surprise. It jumps on us like a murderer in the night.

TOM Then love is like death, you know it will come but you don't know when. Don't you think it is an old-fashioned idea? Of the kind you think about in church?

JEANNE Of the kind you think about in empty apartments.

TOM What do you want to say?

But the saleswoman turns toward Tom with a murderous look. The other girls imitate her and put their index finger in front of their mouths: *Shhhh!*

They move away, and suddenly we see Jeanne, beautiful like a swan in the white triumph of her bridal dress, vaguely reminiscent of the forties. The moment is magical. The cameraman continues to film. Some drops of rain fall.

TOM Jeanne . . . you're superb.

Tom runs outside.

JEANNE Yes . . . the costume creates the bride.

TOM You're better than Rita Hayworth, better than Joan Crawford, better than Kim Novak, better than Lauren Bacall, better than Ava Gardner when she loved Mickey Rooney!

Suddenly it starts raining. Everyone runs to take cover. The cameraman and the sound man take their instruments in the van. Tom and the scriptgirl help them. When Tom goes back in the shop, Jeanne is gone. He searches for her in vain.

SALESWOMAN She was here a moment ago.

It is raining violently.

SCENE 25

INTERIOR: STAIRWAY ELEVATOR; DAY

Jeanne is completely drenched. Her clothes stick to her body. She is sitting on a wooden bench in a niche opposite the elevator. She shivers a little.

The hall is deserted. We hear the rain beating on a tin roof somewhere, and from time to time the sound of distant thunder.

Footsteps. It is Paul. He hardly looks at her; he enters the elevator, leaving the gate open. She follows him. Paul looks at the girl's sopping clothes. She follows his gaze along her own body. She is wearing no bra, and seems nude under the light, wet material.

Paul presses the button.

Panoramic shot to follow the elevator, which moves very slowly, ascending.

Panoramic shot, ascending, like the elevator, from low to high, to follow the edge of Jeanne's skirt and then, little by little, the length of her legs, discovering her knees, her thighs, her naked pubis, up to her belly button, which is the belly button of a little girl. Higher, her face begs forgiveness.

Then the hand of the woman moves forward,

searching for Paul's pants, and crosses Paul's hand in mid-air as he reaches for her vagina. Their arms graze each other, forming a kind of cross.

SCENE 26

INTERIOR: APARTMENT; DAY

They have entered the apartment. Rain is pouring in through a window. Paul goes to close it. Jeanne goes into the living room. Paul carries her to the bed. She hugs the pillow.

JEANNE Forgive me! I wanted to leave you and I couldn't. I can't! Do you still want me?

PAUL (*singing*) There once was a man and he had an old sow . . . You know you're wet.

Her hand encounters something soft, something horribly inert between the pillow and the sheet. For a moment Jeanne doesn't understand; then she looks and screams. The cavernous scream of someone losing control.

Paul runs into the living room. Jeanne stands in the center of the room, paralyzed, trembling. She indicates the bed with her eyes.

Paul goes to look. The shape of a motionless animal stands out against the white sheet. It is a huge, dead rat, soaked in its own blood.

Jeanne shudders. Paul hugs her. The contact seems to revive her. A shiver runs through her. She struggles free of his embrace and, as if disgusted, rushes towards

the front door. But Paul is faster and bolts the door, blocking her way.

JEANNE I want to go. I want to go away!

Paul has no intention of giving in to her hysteria. Once again he reaches out to caress her and calm her, but she breaks away from him.

JEANNE Don't touch me!

PAUL Calm down now.

She speaks in gulps.

JEANNE That horrible thing . . . here . . . in our bed!

PAUL It's nothing but a rat, a dead rat. Paris is full of rats. There are more rats than people. Yum, yum, yum.

He takes her by the hand and leads her into the living room. He seats her in the armchair.

JEANNE I want to go.

PAUL Don't you want a bite first? You don't want to run and eat.

JEANNE This is the end!

He picks up the rat by the tail.

PAUL No, this the end. But I like to start with the head, that's the best part. Now you're sure you won't have any? Okay. What's the matter? You don't dig rat?

JEANNE I want to go. I can't make love in this bed any more. I can't. It's disgusting, nauseating.

PAUL Well, we'll fuck on the radiator or standing on the mantle. Listen, I got to get some mayonnaise for this because it really is good with mayonnaise. I—I'll save the asshole for you. Rat's asshole with mayonnaise. (*laughs*)

JEANNE Oh. I want to get out of here. I want to go away. I can't take it any more here. I'm going away. I'm never coming back, never.

Paul turns the lock. Now Jeanne is free to go. Paul returns to the living room. He goes to the bed and begins to strip off the bloody sheet. Jeanne reappears in the doorway.

JEANNE I forgot to tell you something. I fell in love with somebody.

Paul rolls the sheet into a ball and throws it into the bottom of a wall closet. Then he goes over to the young woman.

PAUL Oh, isn't that wonderful! You know, you're going to have to get out of these wet duds.

He rips off her wet clothing violently.

JEANNE I'm going to make love with him.

PAUL First you have to take a hot bath, 'cause if you don't you're going to get pneumonia, right. And then you know what happens? You die, and I get to fuck the dead rat.

JEANNE Oooooo!

PAUL Give me the soap.

Jeanne is in the bathtub, her head leaning against the back edge, her eyes closed. On his knees, Paul soaps her body. He has rolled up his sleeves to keep them dry. He acts like a father washing his daughter.

JEANNE I'm in love.

PAUL You're in love. How delightful.

JEANNE (*gasps*) I'm in love! (*gasps*) I'm in love, you

understand? (*gasps*) You know, you are old, and you're getting fat.

PAUL Fat, is it? How unkind.

JEANNE Half of your hair is out, and the other half is almost white.

PAUL You know, in ten years you're going to be playing soccer with your tits. What do you think of that?

JEANNE (*gasps*)

PAUL And you know what I'm going to be doing?

JEANNE You'll be in a wheel chair.

PAUL Well, maybe. But you know, I'll be smirking and giggling all the way to eternity.

JEANNE How poetic. But please, before you go, wash my feet.

PAUL Noblesse oblige.

JEANNE Magnificent.

PAUL You know you're a jerk? 'Cause the best fucking you're going to get is right here in this apartment. Stand up.

He takes a large bathtowel and holds it open. Jeanne gets out of the bathtub. Paul wraps her with it and dries her.

JEANNE He is full of mysteries.

PAUL Listen, you dumb dodo, all the mysteries that you're ever going to know in life are right here.

JEANNE He is like everybody, but at the same time, he is different.

PAUL You mean, like everybody.

JEANNE You know, even he frightening . . .

PAUL Huh?

JEANNE Even he frightens me.

PAUL What is he. A local pimp?

JEANNE He could be. He looks it. Do you know why I'm in love with him?

PAUL I can't wait.

JEANNE Because he knows—he knows how to make me fall in love with him.

PAUL And you want this man that you love to protect you and take care of you?

JEANNE Yeah.

PAUL You want this gold and shining powerful warrior to build you a fortress where you can hide in. So you don't have to ever have—have—a-a-a-a—you don't have to feel lonely. You never have to feel empty, that's what you want, isn't it?

JEANNE Yes.

PAUL Well, you'll never find him.

JEANNE But I found this man!

PAUL Well, then it won't be long until he'll want you to build a fortress for him out of your tits, and out of your cunt and out of your hair and your smile— and it's someplace where he can feel—feel comfortable enough and secure enough so that he can worship in front of the altar of his own prick.

JEANNE But I've found this man.

PAUL No, you're alone. You're all alone. And you won't be able to be free of that feeling of being alone until you look death right in the face. I mean, that sounds like bullshit and some romantic crap. Until you go right up into the ass of death—right up his ass—till you find a womb of fear. And then, maybe, maybe then you can—you'll be able to find him.

JEANNE But I've found this man. He's you. You're that man!

PAUL Give me the scissors.

JEANNE What?

PAUL Give me the fingernail scissors. I want you to cut the fingernails on your right hand, these two.

JEANNE That's it.

PAUL I want you to put your fingers up my ass.

Jeanne kneels between Paul's legs. She inserts one, then two, then three fingers into his asshole. Gently, she starts to move her hand, buggering him.

PAUL Put your fingers up my ass, are you deaf? Go on. I'm going to get a pig. And I'm going to—and I'm going to have the pig fuck you. And I want the pig to vomit in your face. And I want you to swallow the vomit. You going to do that for me?

JEANNE Yeah.

PAUL Huh?

JEANNE Yeah!

PAUL And I want the pig to die while—while you're fucking him. And then you have to go behind and I want you to smell the dying farts of the pig. Are you going to do all that for me?

JEANNE Yes, and more than that. And worse. And worse than before.

SCENE 27

Interior: Wall and Stairway, Hotel; Night

What appeared to be a quiet, third-rate hotel seems completely transformed, now, in the middle of the night. Shadows decorate whole walls. The corridors seem endless. Everything that looked like a quaint relic in daylight—everything dusty, old crooked—recovers its unconscious geography at night. The flavor of places explored long ago. A journey into the subconscious, the *déjà-vu*.

Paul moves around like the guardian of a labyrinth, making the rounds of some strange prison. He turns corners. He disappears into shadows, He reappears in a pool of light, there, at the end of the hall, near the stairway: and he spies.

He spies through a series of peepholes that in the wallpaper's leafy patterns are like tiny eyes hidden behind innocent and anonymous landscapes, hidden at the back of empty closets, hidden in the shadows of dead corners.

The hotel is a sort of spider's web. A hole there, another here, through them, it is possible to oversee every being living there, dying there.

Paul sees bodies lost in sleep, figures falling apart in the heat of the night, eyelids of soft stone that seem shut forever, mouths slack with uncontrolled grimaces, lips sunk in nothing but parched air, asses that are only the negation of fleshy roundness, breasts that are old and pale, breasts young and pale, throats that rasp out sudden invocations in sleep, incoherent phrases, spit that dribbles down to the jaw and dries up, old bodies curled in fetal positions. The vision is hallucinating, nightmarish, because sleep has invented anatomies that are definitive and absolute.

All is well in the hotel. Everyone is asleep. And yet, it is with suffering and disgust that Paul recognizes familiar faces. Recognizing them there is like identifying them on a slab at the morgue.

With a certain anxiety Paul turns the key in the lock and enters a somber room. He relocks the door carefully and goes to sit down. He lights a last cigarette and throws the empty packet away. He is tired.

PAUL I just made the rounds. I haven't done it in a long time.

He speaks to someone in front of him, someone we can't see.

PAUL Everything's fine. Quiet.

He tries to search for something on the wall with his fingertips. It is another peephole.

PAUL Here it is. These walls are like Swiss cheese.

Now his eyes are used to the dark. The room is not his room. It is the one decked with flowers and a big bed.
Rosa's corpse lies in the open coffin in a beatific pose. She seems to be laughing in a little lake of flowers. Flowers all along her body, flowers in her hair, in little minuscule bouquets.

PAUL You look ridiculous in that make-up. Like the caricature of a whore. A little touch of mommy in the night. Fake Ophelia drowned in a bathtub. I wish you could see yourself. You'd really laugh. You're your mother's masterpiece. Christ, there are too many fucking flowers in this place, I can't breathe. . . . You know, on top of the closet I found a cardboard box. Inside I found all your little goodies. Pens, key chains, foreign money, French ticklers, the whole shot. Even a clergyman's collar. . . . I didn't know you collected all these little knickknacks left behind.

He speaks to her as if she were alive.

PAUL Even if the husband lives two hundred fucking years, he's never going to be able to discover his wife's real nature. I mean, I might be able to comprehend the universe but I'll never discover the truth about you, never. I mean, who the hell were

you? Remember that day, the first day I was there? I knew that I couldn't get into your pants unless I said—what did I say? Oh yes—"May I have my bill please? I have to leave." Remember? Last night, I ripped off the lights on your mother and the whole joint went bananas. They were all your—your guests, as you used to call them. I guess that includes me, doesn't it? It does include me, doesn't it? For five years I was more of a guest in this fucking flophouse than a husband, with privileges of course. And then to help me understand you, you let me inherit Marcel. The husband's double whose room was the double of ours. And you know what? I didn't even have the guts to ask him. Didn't even have the guts to ask him if the same numbers that you and I did were the same numbers you did with him. Our marriage was nothing more than a foxhole for you. And all it took for you to get out was a thirty-five-cent razor. And a tub full of water.

Now he puts his hands together as if he is praying.

PAUL You cheap, goddam fucking Godforsaken whore —hope you rot in hell! You're worse than the dirtiest street pig that anybody could ever find anywhere and you know why? Because you lied. You lied to me, and I trusted you. You lied. You knew you were lying. Go on, tell me you didn't lie. Haven't you got anything to say about that? You can think up something, can't you? Go on, tell me something. Go on, smile, you cunt. Go on, tell me—tell me something sweet. Smile at me and say it was— I just misunderstood. Go on, tell me you pig-fucker. You goddam fucking pig—fucking liar.

Suddenly he gets up and takes a towel from the bathroom. He wets a corner of it with saliva and gently rubs it on her lips.

PAUL (*sobbing*) I'm sorry. I just can't stand to see these goddam leaves in your face. You never wore make-up—all this fucking shit. I'm going to take this off your mouth. Lipstick.

The rouge disappears little by little, and the lips pale. Paul caresses Rosa's cheek with the palm of his hand, then, as if his energy is diminishing rapidly, he lets himself slide onto his knees; he leans his elbows on the coffin and buries his face in his arms. He cries, his face hidden.

PAUL Rosa, my love . . . forgive me . . . I don't know why you did it. I'd do it too if I knew how. I just don't know. I need to find a way.

A ringing bell is superimposed on his voice. The sound seems very far away. Paul remains immobile for a few minutes, then gets up slowly. The bell continues with a kind of desperate insistence. Paul begins to dress, every gesture tired and mechanical.

PAUL What? All right, I'm coming. I have to go. I have to go, sweetheart baby, someone's calling me.

Two silhouettes in the shadow behind the windows of the locked door. Paul looks at them, they look at him, waiting for him to open up. It is a man and a woman. Impossible to tell more than that, the street is so dark and shadowy.

As is the hotel entrance. Paul doesn't turn on the lights.

Seeing that he hasn't decided to open the door, the woman begins to make signs with her head and her hands to call him over. Her gestures are awkward and slightly grotesque. Paul watches her without moving. Then she starts hanging on the bell again.

The noise invades the deserted hall with exasperating insistence. Paul takes several steps toward the win-

dowed door. The woman's voice is muffled by the glass barrier.

PROSTITUTE Wake up! Open this door!

PAUL It's late. It's four o'clock!

PROSTITUTE I only need the room for an hour, an hour-and-a-half at the most.

PAUL We're filled up.

The woman's gaze runs over the hotel plaque outside.

PROSTITUTE That's not true. When you're full, you hang a sign outside.

Paul can't quite see the man's face, which is partially hidden by the worried looks he keeps sending back at the street.

PROSTITUTE I'm sick of yelling through a door. Call the proprietor, do you hear? What are you waiting for?

Paul opens the door, and the woman enters the shadowy hall with a sigh of relief.

PROSTITUTE You must be new here. I've never seen you before. But don't make trouble or I'll tell your boss.

She moves around as if she is in her own home.

After a moment she remembers her customer and turns to call him.

PROSTITUTE Come on in, it's all arranged.

But the man is no longer there. The woman rushes outside but then returns aggressively to Paul.

PROSTITUTE Are you happy now? You scared him off.

PAUL I'm very sorry.

She takes his arm and pushes him outside.

PROSTITUTE Hurry, he can't be far. Convince him to come back. Tell him he can't just leave.

Paul begins to walk down the deserted street.

PROSTITUTE Run! Don't let him get away!

So Paul is on his way to retrieve the client who has changed his mind about the old whore.

SCENE 28

EXTERIOR: AROUND THE HOTEL; NIGHT

Little streets, alleys that the night strips and skins like a stage set about to be torn down.
Paul walks rapidly, looking around. His eyes search

the dark corners, the niches of doorways. Nothing. By now he has practically circled the street. He stops all of a sudden. He has discovered him.

PAUL Come here . . . Come out of there.

Paul approaches the subway entrance. There is the man he's been hunting for. He is hiding on the subway stairs. Only his head shows above the street level, as if he is standing in a hole. An anonymous, frightened face.

CUSTOMER Please, I beg you, tell her you couldn't find me.

PAUL What's the matter with you?

CUSTOMER I don't feel like it anymore. Did you get a look at her face?

The man grimaces significantly.

CUSTOMER Please don't say you found me. Did you see how ugly she is?

He makes a gesture with his head as if to say, "I could kick myself."

CUSTOMER Once my wife was enough for me. But she caught this skin disease a year ago. Just like that. All of a sudden her skin became disgusting. Like snakeskin. What am I supposed to do?

Paul grabs him and slams him up against the wall.

CUSTOMER Let me go! You're crazy! Let me go!

PAUL Now get the fuck out of here! Faggot!

SCENE 29

Interior: Hotel; Night

The woman is sitting on a divan in the shadows. She is smoking a cigarette when she sees Paul reappear, alone. He sits on the divan facing her.

PROSTITUTE I knew it. First you let him get away, then you can't get him back.

PAUL Want something to drink?

PROSTITUTE Where am I to find another one? At this hour.

Paul searches in his jacket for some money.

PAUL How much did I cost you? A hundred francs okay?

The woman laughs loudly in the shadows.

PROSTITUTE A hundred . . . two hundred . . . give me what you can. I don't do it for the money. I like it, you understand? You know you're cute? Come sit here.

Paul doesn't move. She hums the beginning of a song.

PROSTITUTE They say I have a beautiful voice. If you want, we can do it here. I'm wearing a practical dress. The zipper opens all the way. I don't even need to take it off. Come on, don't be shy . . .

Paul turns on the light. She didn't expect it, and is shocked. She and Paul look at each other. It is a death mask there, not a face, and this body isn't a body but a skeleton. So Paul thinks. And the woman senses it. She stands up all at once and closes her dress. Disgust envelops her expression from the eyes to the mouth.

PROSTITUTE Don't look at me like that. I'm not young anymore. So what? Your wife will be just like me one day.

SCENE 30

INTERIOR: APARTMENT; DAY

Jeanne opens the door with her key. She has hardly entered when she stops short, shocked. The sensation becomes more precise. The apartment is empty, like the first time we saw it. The light is just about the same as then. The girl goes through the apartment without expression. All the furniture is gone, except for the red record player, which sits on the bare floor.

SCENE 31

INTERIOR: FRONT HALL BUILDING ON RUE JULES VERNE, CONCIERGE'S CUBBYHOLE; DAY.

The old concierge, as shriveled as ever, her back to her window, shakes her head. Jeanne is very close to the window.

JEANNE Try to remember. The man on the fifth floor? He's been living there for the last few days.

CONCIERGE I don't see anybody, I tell you. They

come . . . they leave. I recognize your voice though.
You came a couple of days ago.

JEANNE I have to send the key. Where are you for-
warding the mail? Give me the address.

CONCIERGE I don't have an address. I don't know
these people.

JEANNE Not even his name?

CONCIERGE Nothing. You wouldn't have a cigarette?

Jeanne leaves without replying. She remains an instant, leaning on the wall, then suddenly dashes toward
the bar.

SCENE 32

INTERIOR: BAR, TELEPHONE BOOTH; DAY

Jeanne is on the telephone, like the first time. She
is talking to Tom and trying hard to conceal her anxiety.

JEANNE I found an apartment for us. One rue Jules
Verne . . . Yes, in Passy. Come right away. I'll wait
for you . . . Fifth floor.

Tom hangs up. Jeanne has a sudden sob. Not a sob,
a moan.

SCENE 33

Jeanne is waiting to show Tom the apartment.

JEANNE Come in. It's open . . . You like our apartment? It's full of light. There's one room too small for a big bed. Maybe for a baby. Fidel. Nice name for a kid. Fidel. Like Castro.

TOM But I want a daughter too. Rosa. Like Rosa Luxembourg. She's not as well known, but she's not bad . . . I wanted to film you every day. In the morning when you wake up, then when you fall asleep. When you smile the first time. And I didn't film anything. Today we finish shooting. The film is finished. I don't like things that finish. One must begin something else right away . . . But it's huge! Where are you?

JEANNE I'm here.

TOM You could get lost in here!

JEANNE Oh, stop it.

TOM How'd you find it?

JEANNE By chance.

TOM We'll change everything.

JEANNE We'll change chance to fate.

Tom's hands become a mock camera.

TOM Come forward! Take off! Fly. Fly. You're in heaven! You rise up. You are in heaven. Now dive! Make three turns. Descend. What's happening to me? An air pocket . . .

JEANNE What's happening to you?

TOM Enough of these turbulent zones. We can't joke like this . . . like children. We're adults.

JEANNE Adults? That's terrible.

TOM Yes, it's terrible.

JEANNE Then how must we act?

TOM I don't know. Invent gestures, words . . . For example, one thing I do know. Adults are serious, logical, circumspect, hairy . . . They all face problems. Here, this apartment is not for us. Absolutely not.

JEANNE Where are you going?

TOM To look for another.

JEANNE Another like what?

TOM One you can live in.

JEANNE But you can live here.

TOM I find this sad. It smells. Come with me?

JEANNE I have to close the windows, give back the keys. Leave it all in order . . . So long.

TOM So long.

Tom leaves. After a moment Jeanne gets up. She goes to close all the shutters.

SCENE 34

EXTERIOR: STREETS OF PARIS; DAY

Jeanne walks on rue Jules Verne very slowly. The street is deserted. She feels the sound of feet following her but does not turn around. Then a hand reaches under her arm for her hand. It is Paul.

This is the first time they are together outside their island. It is their first contact with reality. They walk for a while, holding hands. Rare pedestrians look at them and then keep on walking briskly. Without saying a word Paul embraces her.

They hang on to each other.

They walk together bent slightly forward as if struggling against a wind . . . which isn't blowing. They look a little afraid. Then Paul's hands move up to Jeanne's body to her neck, the back of her head, her ears. He touches her cheeks with his hands gently, as if afraid of breaking her, and kisses her.

At the sound of an approaching car Jeanne breaks out of the embrace, and drags Paul down the stairs of the subway. Now they are hidden. They kiss unafraid. Now they are standing up, alone in a subway car. In a tight embrace, cheek against cheek, they see the dark of the tunnel approaching, then rapidly again daylight comes back. It is an elevated subway. They start kissing again.

PAUL It's me again.

JEANNE It's over.

PAUL Yes, it's over. Then it begins again.

JEANNE What begins again? I don't understand anything any more.

PAUL Well, there's nothing to understand. We left the apartment, and now we begin again with love and all the rest of it.

JEANNE The rest?

There's a sweetness in his voice that we haven't heard before.

PAUL Yeah. Listen, I'm forty-five. I'm a widower. I've got a little hotel that's kind of a dump but it's not completely a flophouse. I used to live on my luck— then I got married. My wife killed herself. But you know, what the hell. I'm no prize. I picked up a nail when I was in Cuba in nineteen forty-eight and now I've got a prostate like an Idaho potato. But I'm still a good stick man even if I can't have any children. Let's see. I don't have any stamping grounds, I don't have any friends, and I suppose if I hadn't met you I'd probably settle for a hard chair and a hemorrhoid . . . Anyway, to make a long, dull story even duller, I come from a time when a guy like me would drop into a joint like this and pick up a young chick like you and call her a bimbo.

SCENE 35

INTERIOR: BAR, DANCING; DAY

The place is very sad. Jeanne is hiding behind the large lenses of her dark glasses. Behind them, in the room, there is a small tango contest. The jury, in front of a long table, follow with their eyes the couples dancing with numbers on their backs.

Paul and Jeanne have on their table a bottle of champagne, half full, and a bottle of whisky. Pauls seems very excited.

PAUL I'm awfully sorry to intrude but I was so struck with your beauty that I thought I would offer you a glass of champagne. Is this seat taken?

JEANNE No.

PAUL May I?

JEANNE If you'd like to.

PAUL You know the tango is a rite, and, you understand, "rite"? And you must watch the legs of the dancers . . . You haven't drunk your champagne because it was warm. Then I ordered you a Scotch, and you haven't drunk your Scotch . . . Now come on. Just a sip for Daddy.

Jeanne takes her glass and sips.

PAUL Now, if you love me, you'll drink all of it.

She empties the glass in one gulp.

JEANNE Okay, I love you.

PAUL Bravo.

JEANNE Tell me about your wife.

PAUL Let's talk about us.

Jeanne speaks with an enormous fatigue.

JEANNE But this place is so pitiful.

PAUL Yes, but I'm here, aren't I?

JEANNE Monsier Maître d'Hotel.

PAUL That's rather nasty. Anyway, you dummy, I love you and I want to live with you.

JEANNE In your flophouse?

PAUL In my flophouse. What the hell does that mean? What the hell difference does it make if I have a flophouse or a hotel or a castle? I love you! What the fuck difference does it make? I'll sell it.

PRESIDENT OF THE TANGO JURY The jury has chosen . . . The following ten best couples: Number three, seven, eight, nine, eleven, twelve, thirteen, fourteen, fifteen, and nineteen. Now gentlemen, ladies, all best wishes for the last tango!

JEANNE Give me some more whisky.

PAUL Oh, I thought you weren't drinking.

JEANNE Well, I'm thirsty now, and I want some more drink.

PAUL All right.

She empties her glass. They go to the dance floor. She abandons herself completely in his arms. They kiss. The music ends. They return to their table. Jeanne is a bit unsteady on her feet.

PAUL I think that's a good idea. Wait a minute be-be-because you're really beautiful. Wait a minute.

JEANNE Okay.

PAUL I'm sorry, I'm terribly sorry. I didn't mean to spill my drink.

JEANNE Well, let's have a toast to our life in the hotel.

PAUL No, fuck all that. Come on. Let's drink a toast to our life in the country, yeah?

JEANNE You're a nature lover? You never told me that.

PAUL Oh, for Chri . . . I'm nature boy. Can't you see me with the cows? And the chickenshit all over me?

JEANNE Oh yeah.

PAUL Hum?

JEANNE To the house and the cows. I will be your cow, too.

PAUL And listen, I get to milk you twice a day. How about that?

JEANNE I hate the country.

PAUL What do you mean, you hate the country?

JEANNE I hate it. I prefer to go to the hotel. Come on, let's go to the hotel.

PAUL Let's dance. Come on. Let's dance. Come on. Don't you want to dance?

They move to the dance floor and dance outrageously.

PRESIDENT OF THE TANGO JURY Out! What are you doing? It's impossible.

PAUL It's love! Always . . .

PRESIDENT OF THE TANGO JURY But it's a contest. Where's love fit in? Go to the movies to see love!

They go back to a table.

PAUL Beauty of mine, sit before me. Let me peruse you and remember you always like this.

JEANNE Oh!

PAUL Waiter, champagne! If music be the food of love, play on! What's the matter with you?

JEANNE It's finished.

PAUL What's the matter with you?

JEANNE It's finished.

PAUL What's finished?

JEANNE We're never going to see each other again, never.

PAUL That's ridiculous. That's ridiculous.

JEANNE It's not a joke.

PAUL (*jokingly*) Oh, you dirty rat!

JEANNE It's finished.

PAUL Look, when something's finished, it begins again, you see?

JEANNE I'm getting married. I'm going away. It's finished.

She slides her hand on Paul's thigh until it disappears under the table. She stares straight into his eyes.

PAUL Oh Jesus! Look, that's not a subway strap, that's me cock!

JEANNE It's finished.

With her other hand, she opens her purse and takes out a handkerchief. She dries her hand quickly. Now she doesn't even have the courage to look him in the face. She leaves rapidly.

PAUL Wait a minute! You dumb bimbo! Shit! Wait a minute! Goddamnit! Hey, rube! Come here! Come here! I'm going to get you, bimbo.

SCENE 36

Exterior: Street, Jeanne's Home; Day

Paul walks a dozen feet behind Jeanne. From time to time the woman turns around and glances at him. She tries to lose him. Paul follows her, always keeping his distance.

Now she is in front of her house.

Paul approaches her.

JEANNE Stop! Stop!

PAUL Hold it!

JEANNE Enough!

PAUL Hey, cool it! Listen.

JEANNE Enough! It's over! Go away! Go away!

PAUL I can't win! Give me a break! Hey, dummy!

She gets away from him and enters the building, running. She shuts herself in the elevator. Paul throws himself up the stairs, watching the elevator at every landing. He glimpses Jeanne's face four times through the elevator's glass door. Her mouth is tense in a grimace of fear.

The elevator stops just as Paul reaches the floor, breathless. He bars her way. She has her keys clenched and ready in her hand.

JEANNE I'll call the police!

PAUL I smell the hen house. Well, shit, I'm not in your way. I mean, *après vous*, Mademoiselle. So, so long, sister. Besides you're a crummy-looking broad. I don't give a damn if I never see you again. Shit!

JEANNE Enough! Enough!

PAUL Oh, fuck the police!

JEANNE You're crazy!

PAUL Listen, I want to talk to you.

JEANNE Help! Help!

PAUL Now this is getting ridiculous.

JEANNE Help!

Jeanne manages to get to her door. She enters, screaming. Paul follows her in. Her mother isn't there. But signs of the wedding are visible everywhere.

PAUL This is the title shot, baby. We're going all the way. It's a little old. But full of memory now. How do you like your hero? Over easy or sunny-side up? You ran through Africa and Asia and Indonesia. Now I've found you. And I love you. I want to know your name.

Jeanne has retreated as far as her mother's bedroom. Now she doesn't scream anymore; now she cries. Crying, she opens the wooden box; crying, she takes out the dueling pistol; crying, she points it at Paul. Crying, she fires.

JEANNE Jeanne.

People appear in the doorway, but we don't see them. We only hear frightened voices. After a few seconds, Jeanne comes out of the bedroom with the pistol in her hand. Paul staggers onto a balcony . . .

PAUL Our children. Our children. Our children. Will remember . . .

And dies.

JEANNE   I don't know who he is. He followed me on
the street. He tried to rape me. He's a madman. I
don't know his name. I don't know his name. I don't
know who he is . . . He wanted to rape me. I don't
know. I don't know him. I don't know who he is.
He's a madman. I don't know his name.

Now Jeanne isn't crying anymore.

[END]

A TRANSIT TO NARCISSUS

by NORMAN MAILER

To pay one's $5.00 and join the full house at the Trans Lux for the evening show of *Last Tango in Paris* is to be reminded once again that the planet is in a state of pullulation. The reasons accelerate. The snow which was falling in November had left by the first of March. Would our summer arrive at Easter and end with July? It is all that nuclear radiation, says every aficionado of the occult. And we pullulate. Like an ant-hive beginning to feel the heat.

We know that Spengler's thousand-year metamorphosis from Culture to Civilization is gone, way gone, and the century required for a minor art to move from commencement to decadence is off the board. Whole fashions in film arc born, thrive, and die in twenty-four months. Still! It is only a half year since Pauline Kael declared to the readers of *The New Yorker* that the presentation of *Last Tango in Paris* at the New York Film Festival on October 14, 1972, was a date which "should become a landmark in movie history—comparable to May 29, 1913—the night *Le Sacre du Printemps* was first performed—in music history," and then went on to explain that the newer work had "the same kind of hypnotic excitement as the *Sacre,* the same primitive force, and the same jabbing, thrusting eroticism. . . . Bertolucci and Brando have altered the face of an art form." Whatever could have been shown on screen to make Kael pop open for a film? "This must be the most powerfully erotic movie ever made, and it may turn out to be the most liberating movie ever made. . . ." Could this be our own Lady Vinegar, our quintessential cruet? The first frigid of the film critics was treating us to her first public reception. Prophets of Baal, praise Kael! We had obviously no ordinary hour of cinema to contemplate.

Now, a half year later, the movie is history, has all the palpability of the historic. Something just discernible has already happened to humankind as a result of it, or, at least to that audience who are coming in to the Trans Lux to see it. They are a crew. They have unexpected homogeneity for a movie audience, compose, indeed, so thin a sociological slice of the New York and suburban sausage that you cannot be sure your own ticket isn't what was left for the toothpick, while the rest of the house has been bought at a bite. At the least, there is the same sense of aesthetic oppression one feels at a play when the house is filled with a theater party. So, too, is the audience at *Tango* an infarct of middle-class anal majesties—if Freud hadn't given us the clue, a reader of faces could decide all on his own that there had to be some social connection between sex, shit, power, violence, and money. But these middle-class faces have advanced their historical inch from the last time one has seen them. They are this much closer now to late Romans.

Whether matrons or young matrons, men or boys,

they are *swingers*. The males have wife-swapper mustaches, the women are department-store boutique. It is as if everything recently and incongruously idealistic in the middle class has been used up in the years of resistance to the Vietnamese War—now, bring on the Caribbean. Amazing! In America, even the Jews have come to look like the French middle class, which is to say that the egocentricity of the Fascist mouth is on the national face. Perhaps it is the five-dollar admission, but this audience has an obvious obsession with sex as the confirmed core of a wealthy life. It is enough to make one ashamed of one's own obsession (although where would one delineate the difference?). Maybe it is that this audience, still in March, is suntanned, or at least made up to look suntanned. The red and orange of their skins will match the famous "all uterine" colors—so termed by the set designer—of the interiors in *Last Tango*.

In the minute before the theater lights are down, what a tension is in the house. One might as well be in the crowd just before an important fight commences. It is years since one has watched a movie begin with such anticipation. And the tension holds as the projection starts. We see Brando and Schneider pass each other in the street. Since we have all been informed—by *Time* no less—we know they are going to take carnal occupation of each other, and very soon. The audience watches with anxiety as if it is also going to be in the act with someone new, and the heart (and for some, the bowels) is in tremors between earthquake and expectation. Maria Schneider is so sexual a presence. None of the photographs has prepared anybody for this. Rare actresses, just a few, have flesh appeal. You feel as if you can touch them on the screen. Schneider has nose appeal

—you can smell her. She is every eighteen-year-old in a mini-skirt and a maxi-coat who ever promenaded down Fifth Avenue in that inner arrogance which proclaims, "My cunt is my chariot."

We have no more than a few minutes to wait. She goes to look at an apartment for rent, Brando is already there. They have passed in the street, and by a telephone booth; now they are in an empty room. Abruptly Brando cashes the check Stanley Kowalski wrote for us twenty-five years ago—he fucks the heroine standing up. It solves the old snicker of how do you do it in a telephone booth?—he rips her panties open. In our new line of *New Yorker*-approved superlatives, it can be said that the cry of the fabric is the most thrilling sound to be heard in World Culture since the four opening notes of Beethoven's Fifth.[1] It is, in fact, a hell of a sound, small, but as precise as the flash of a match above a pile of combustibles, a way for the director to say, "As you may already have guessed from the way I established my opening, I am very good at movie making, and I have a superb pair, Brando and Schneider—they are sexual heavyweights. Now I place my director's promise upon the material: you are going to be in for a grave and wondrous experience. We are going to get to the bottom of a man and a woman."

So intimates Bertolucci across the silence of that room, as Brando and Schneider, fully dressed, lurch, grab, connect, hump, scream, and are done in less than a minute,

[1] John Simon, as predictable in his critical reactions as a headwaiter, naturally thought *Last Tango* was part of the riff-raff. Since it is Simon's temper to ignore details, he not only does not hear the panties tearing (some ears reside in the music of the spheres) but announces that Schneider, beasty abomination, is wearing none.

their orgasms coming on top of one another like trash cans tumbling down a hill. They fall to the floor, and fall apart. It is as if a hand grenade has gone off in their entrails. A marvelous scene, good as a passionate kiss in real life, then not so good because there has been no shot of Brando going up Schneider, and since the audience has been watching in all the somber awe one would bring to the first row of a medical theater, it is like seeing an operation without the entrance of the surgeon's knife.

One can go to any hard-core film and see fifty phalluses going in and out of as many vaginas in four hours (if anyone can be found who stayed four hours). There is a monumental abstractedness about hard core. It is as if the more a player can function sexually before a camera, the less he is capable of offering any other expression. Finally, the sexual organs show more character than the actors' faces. One can read something of the working conditions of a life in some young girl's old and irritated cunt, one can even see triumphs of the human spirit—old and badly burned labia which still come to glisten with new life, capital! There are phalluses in porno whose distended veins speak of the integrity of the hardworking heart, but there is so little specific content in the faces! Hard core lulls after it excites, and finally it puts the brain to sleep.

But Brando's real cock up Schneider's real vagina would have brought the history of film one huge march closer to the ultimate experience it has promised since its inception (which is to re-embody life). One can even see how on opening night at the Film Festival, it did not matter so much. Not fully prepared for what was to come, the simulated sex must have quivered like real sex the first time out. Since then we have been told the movie is great, so we are prepared to resist greatness, and have read in *Time* that Schneider said, " 'We were never screwing on stage. I never felt any sexual attraction for him . . . he's almost fifty you know, and'—she runs her hand from her torso to her midriff, 'he's only beautiful to here!' "

So one watches differently. Yes, they *are* simulating. Yes, there is something slightly unnatural in the way they come and fall apart. It is too stylized, as if paying a few subtle respects to Kabuki. The real need for the real cock of Brando into the depths of the real actress might have been for those less exceptional times which would follow the film long after it opened and the reaction had set in.

Since *Tango* is, however, the first major film with a respectable budget, a superbly skilled young director, an altogether accomplished cameraman, and a great actor that is ready to do more than dabble in improvisation, indeed will enter heavily into such near to untried movie science, so the laws of improvisation are before us, and the first law to recognize is that it is next to impossible to build on too false a base. The real problem in movie improvisation is to find some ending which is true to what has gone before and yet is sufficiently untrue to enable the actors to get out alive.

We will come back to that. It is, however, hardly time to let go of our synopsis. Real or simulated, opening night or months later, we know after five minutes that, at the least, we are in for a thoroughgoing study of a man and a woman, and the examination will be close. Brando rents the empty apartment; they will visit each other there every day. His name is Paul, hers is Jeanne, but they are not to learn each other's names yet. They are not to tell one another such things, he informs her.

"We don't need names here . . . we're going to forget everything we knew. . . . Everything outside this place is bullshit."

They are going to search for pleasure. We are back in the existential confrontation of the century. Two people are going to fuck in a room until they arrive at a transcendent recognition or some death of themselves. We are dealing not with a plot but with a theme that is open range for a hundred films. Indeed we are face to face with the fundamental structure of porno—the difference is that we have a director who by the measure of porno is Eisenstein, and actors who are as gods. So the film takes up the simplest and richest of structures. To make love in an empty apartment, then return to a separate life. It is like every clandestine affair the audience has ever had, only more so—no names! Every personal demon will be scourged in the sex—one will obliterate the past! That is the huge sanction of anonymity. It is equal to a new life.

What powerful biographical details we learn, however, on the instant they part. Paul's wife is a suicide. Just the night before, she has killed herself with a razor in a bathtub; the bathroom is before us, red as an abattoir. A sobbing chambermaid cleans it while she speaks in fear to Paul. It is not even certain whether the wife is a suicide or he has killed her—that is almost not the point. It is the bloody death suspended above his life like a bleeding amputated existence—it is with that crimson torso between his eyes that he will make love on the following days.

Jeanne, in her turn, is about to be married to a young TV director. She is the star in a videofilm he is making about French youth. She pouts, torments her fiancé, delights in herself, delights in the special idiocy of men.

She can cuckold her young director to the roots of his eyes. She also delights in the violation she will make of her own bourgeois roots. In this TV film she makes within the movie she presents her biography to her fiancé's camera: she is the daughter of a dead Army officer who was sufficiently racist to teach his dog to detect Arabs by smell. So she is well brought up—there are glimpses of a suburban villa on a small walled estate —it is nothing less than the concentrated family honor of the French army she will surrender when Brando proceeds a little later to bugger her.

These separate backgrounds divide the film as neatly between biography and fornication as those trick high-ball glasses which present a drawing of a man or a woman wearing clothes on the outside of the tumbler and nude on the inside. Each time Brando and Schneider leave the room we learn more of their lives beyond the room; each time they come together, we are ready to go further. In addition, as if to enrich his theme for students of film, Bertolucci offers touches from the history of French cinema. The life preserver in *Atalante* appears by way of homage to Vigo, and Jean-Pierre Léaud of *The 400 Blows* is the TV director, the boy now fully grown. Something of the brooding echo of *Le Jour Se Lève* and Arletty is also with us, that somber memory of Jean Gabin wandering along the wet docks in the dawn, waiting for the police to pick him up after he has murdered his beloved. It is as if we are to think not only of this film but of other sexual tragedies French cinema has brought us, until the sight of each gray and silent Paris street is ready to evoke the lost sound of the *Bal musette* and the sad near-silent wash of the Seine. Nowhere as in Paris can doomed lovers succeed in passing sorrow, drop by drop, through the blood of the audience's heart.

Yet as the film progresses with every skill in evidence, while Brando gives a performance which is unforgettable (and Schneider shows every promise of becoming a major star), as the historic buggeries and reamings are delivered, and the language breaks through barriers not even yet erected—no general of censorship could know the armies of obscenity were so near!—as these shocks multiply, and lust goes up the steps to love, something bizarre happens to the film. It fails to explode. It is a warehouse of dynamite and yet something goes wrong with the blow-up.

One leaves the theater bewildered. A fuse was never ignited. But where was it located? One looks to retrace the line of the story.

So we return to Paul trying to rise out of the bloody horizon of his wife's death. We even have some instinctive comprehension of how he must degrade his beautiful closet-fuck, indeed we are even given the precise detail that he will grease her ass with butter before he buggers her family pride. A scene or two later, he tricks forth her fear of him by dangling a dead rat which he offers to eat. "I'll save the asshole for you," he tells her. "Rat's asshole with mayonnaise."[2] (The audience roars —Brando knows audiences.) She is standing before him in a white wedding gown—she has run away from a TV camera crew which was getting ready to film her pop wedding. She has rushed to the apartment in the rain. Now shivering, but recovered from her fear, she tells him she has fallen in love with somebody. He tells her

[2] The final screenplay was of course not entirely written in advance, but was in part suggested to the actors, and in other places is a transcription after the fact of the full improvisation. In other words, a small but important part of the screenplay has in effect been written by Brando and Schneider.

to take a hot bath, or she'll catch pneumonia, die, and all he'll get is "to fuck the dead rat."

No, she protests, she's in love.

"In ten years," says Brando looking at her big breasts, "you're going to be playing soccer with your tits." But the thought of the other lover is grinding away at him. "Is he a good fucker?"

"Magnificent."

"You know, you're a jerk. 'Cause the best fucking you're going to get is right here in this apartment."

No, no, she tells him, the lover is wonderful, a mystery . . . different.

"A local pimp?"

"He could be. He looks it."

She will never, he tells her, be able to find love until she goes "right up into the ass of death." He is one lover who is not afraid of metaphor. "Right up his ass—till you find a womb of fear. And then maybe you'll be able to find him."

"But I've found this man," says Jeanne. Metaphor has continued long enough for her. "He's you. You're that man."

In the old scripted films, such a phrase was plucked with a movie composer's chord. But this is improvisation. Brando's instant response is to tell her to get a scissors and cut the fingernails on her right hand. Two fingers will do. Put those fingers up his ass.

"*Quoi?*"

"Put your fingers up my ass, are you deaf? Go on."

No, he is not too sentimental. Love is never flowers, but farts and flowers. Plus every superlative test. So we see Brando's face before us—it is that tragic angelic mask of incommunicable anguish which has spoken to us across the years of his uncharted heroic depth. Now

he is entering that gladiator's fundament again, and before us and before millions of faces yet to come she will be his surrogate bugger, real or simulated. What an entrance into the final images of history! He speaks to us with her body behind him, and her fingers just conceivably up him. "I'm going to get a pig," are the words which come out of his tragic face, "and I'm going to have a pig fuck you"—yes, the touch on his hole has broken open one gorgon of a fantasy—"and I want the pig to vomit in your face. And I want you to swallow the vomit. You going to do that for me?"

"Yeah."

"Huh?"

"Yeah!"

"And I want the pig to die while"—a profound pause —"while you're fucking him. And then you have to go behind, and I want you to smell the dying farts of the pig. Are you going to do that for me?"

"Yes, and more than that. And worse than before."

He has plighted a troth. In our year of the twentieth century how could we ever contract for love with less than five hundred pounds of pig shit? With his courage to give himself away, we finally can recognize the tragedy of his expression across these twenty-five years. That expression has been locked into the impossibility of ever communicating such a set of private thoughts through his beggar's art as an actor. Yet he has just done it. He is probably the only actor in the world who could have done it, but then nothing less than *The Godfather* would have enabled him to be in such a position. His metaphor is not filled with shit for too little. He has been living in it. Pus, poop, and Puzo. Now, Brando is scourging himself. He is taking the shit that is in him and leaving it on us. How the audience loves it. They have come to be covered. The world is not polluted for nothing. There is some profound twentieth-century malfunction in the elimination of waste. And Brando is on to it. A stroke of genius to have made a speech like that. Over and over, he is saying in this film that one only arrives at love by springing out of the shit in oneself.

So he seeks to void his eternal waste over the wife's suicide. He sits by her laid-out corpse in a grim hotel room, curses her, weeps, proceeds to wipe off the undertaker's lipstick, broods on her lover (who lives upstairs in the hotel), and goes through some bend of the obscure, for now, off-stage, he proceeds to remove his furniture from the new apartment. We realize this as we see Jeanne in the empty rooms. Paul has disappeared. He has ordered her to march into the farts of the pig for nothing. So she calls her TV director to look at the empty apartment—should they rent it? The profound practicality of the French bourgeoisie is squatting upon us. She appreciates the value of a few memories to offer sauce for her lean marriage. But the TV director must smell this old cooking for he takes off abruptly after telling her he will look for a better apartment.

Suddenly Brando is before her again on the street. Has he been waiting for her to appear? He looks rejuvenated. "It's over," she tells him. "It's over," he replies. "Then it begins again." He is in love with her. He reveals his biography, his dead wife, his unromantic details. "I've got a prostate like an Idaho potato but I'm still a good stick man. . . . I suppose if I hadn't met you I'd probably settle for a hard chair and a hemorrhoid." They move on to a hall, some near mythical species of tango palace where a dance contest is taking place. They get drunk and go on the floor. Brando goes in for a squalid parody of the tango. When they're removed by the judges, he flashes his bare ass. He is still mooning on *The Godfather*.

Now they sit down again and abruptly the love affair is terminated. Like that! She is bored with him. Something has happened. We do not know what. Is she a bourgeoise repelled by his flophouse? Or did his deface-ment of the tango injure some final nerve of upper French deportment? Too small a motive. Must we de-cide that sex without a mask is no longer love, or con-clude upon reflection that no mask is more congenial to passion than to be without a name in the bed of a strange lover?

There are ten reasons why her love could end, but we know none of them. She merely wants to be rid of him. Deliver me from a fifty-year-old, may even be her only cry.

She tries to flee. He follows. He follows her on the Métro and all the way to her home. He climbs the spiral-ing stairs as she mounts in the slow elevator, he rams into her mother's apartment with her, breathless, chewing gum, leering. Now he is all cock. He is the memory of every good fuck he has given her. "This is the title shot, baby. We're going all the way."

She takes out her father's army pistol and shoots him. He murmurs, "Our children, our children, our children will remember . . ." and staggers out to the balcony, looks at the Paris morning, takes out his chewing gum, fixes it carefully to the underside of the iron railing in a move which is pure broth of Brando—culture is a goat turd on the bust of Goethe—and dies. The angel with the tragic face slips off the screen. And proud Maria Schneider is suddenly and most unbelievably reduced to a twat copping a plea. "I don't know who he is," she mutters in her mind to the oncoming *flics*, "he followed me in the street, he tried to rape me, he is insane. I do not know his name. I do not know who he is. He wanted to rape me."

The film ends. The questions begin. We have been treated to more cinematic breakthrough than any film— at the least—since *I Am Curious, Yellow*. In fact we have gone much further. It is hard to think of any film which has taken a larger step. Yet if this is "the most powerful erotic film ever made" then sex is as Ex-Lax to the lady. For we have been given a bath in shit with no reward. The film, for all its power, has turned inside out by the end. We have been asked to follow two serious and more or less desperate lovers as they go through the locks of lust and defecation, through some modern species of homegrown cancer cure, if you will, and have put up with their modern depths—shit on the face of the beloved and find love!—only to discover a peculiar extortion in the aesthetic. We have been taken on this tour down to the prostate big as an Idaho potato only to recognize that we never did get into an exploration of the catacombs of love, passion, infancy, sodomy, tenderness, and the breaking of emotional ice, instead only wandered from one onanist's oasis to another.

It is, however, a movie that has declared itself, by the power of its opening, as equal in experience to a great fuck, and so the measure of its success or failure is by the same sexual aesthetic. Rarely has a film's value depended so much on the power or lack of power of its ending, even as a fuck which is full of promise is ready to be pinched by a poor end. So, in *Tango*, there is no gathering of forces for the conclusion, no whirling of sexual destinies (in this case, the audience and the actors) into the same funnel of becoming, no flying out of the senses in pursuit of a new vision, no, just the full charge into a blank wall, a masturbator's spasm—came for the wrong reason and on the wrong thought—and one is thrown back, shattered, too ubiquitously electrified, and full of criticism for the immediate past. Now the recollected flaws of the film eat at the pleasure, even as the failed orgasm of a passionate act will call the character of the passion into question.

So the walk out of the theater is with anger. The film has been in reach of the greatness Kael has been talking about, but the achievement has only been partial. Like all executions less divine than their conception *Tango* will give rise to mutations which are obliged to explore into dead ends. More aesthetic pollution to come! The performance by Brando has been unique, historic, without compare—it is just possible, however, that it has gone entirely in the wrong direction. He has been like a lover who keeps telling consummate dirty jokes until the ravaged dawn when the girl will say, "Did you come to sing or to screw?" He has come with great honor and dignity and exceptional courage to bare his soul. But in a solo. We are being given a fuck film without the fuck. It is like a Western without the horses.

Now the subtle sense of displacement which has hung over the movie is clear. There has been no particular high passion loose. Brando is so magnetic an actor, Schneider is so attractive, and the scenes are so intimate that we assume there is sexual glue between their parts, but it is our libido which has been boiling that glue and not the holy vibration of the actors on the screen. If Kael has had a sexual liberation with *Tango*, her libido is not alone—the audience is also getting their kicks—by digging the snots of the celebrated. (Liberation for the Silent Majority may be not to attend a fuck but hear dirty jokes.) So the real thrill of *Tango* for $5.00 audiences becomes the peephole Brando offers us on Brando. They are there to hear a world-famous actor say in reply to "What strong arms you have,"

"The better to squeeze a fart out of you."

"What long nails you have."

"The better to scratch your ass with."

"Oh, what a lot of fur you have."

"The better to let your crabs hide in."

"Oh, what a long tongue you have."

"The better to stick in your rear, my dear."

"What's this for?"

"That's your happiness and my ha-penis."

Pandemonium of pleasure in the house. Who wants to watch an act of love when the ghost of Lenny Bruce is back? The crowd's joy is that a national celebrity is being obscene on screen. To measure the media magnetism of such an act, ask yourself how many hundreds of miles you might drive to hear Richard Nixon speak a line like: "We're just taking a flying fuck at a rolling doughnut," or "I went to the University of the Congo; studied whale fucking." Only liberal unregenerates would be so progressive as to say they would not drive a mile. No, one would start mass migrations if Nixon were to give Brando's pig-and-vomit address to the test of love.

Let us recognize the phenomenon. It would be so surrealistic an act, we could not pass Nixon by. Surrealism has become our objective correlative. A private glimpse of the great becomes the alchemy of the media, the fool's gold of the century of communication. In the age of television we know everything about the great but how they fart—the ass wind is, ergo, our trade wind. It is part of Brando's genius to recognize that the real interest of audiences is not having him portray the tender passages and murderous storms of an unruly passion between a man and a woman, it is rather to be given a glimpse of his kinks. His kinks offer sympathetic vibration to their kinks. The affirmation of passion is that we rise from the swamps of our diapers—by whatever torturous route—to the cock and the cunt; it is the acme of the decadent to go from the first explosive bout of love in *Tango* down to the trimmed fingernails up his rectum.

Then follows the murder. Except it does not follow. It has been placed there from the beginning as the required ending in Bertolucci's mind, it has already been written into the screenplay first prepared with Trintignant and Dominique Sanda in mind. But complications and cast changes occurred. Sanda was pregnant, et cetera. Brando appeared, and Schneider was found. Yet the old ending is still there. Since it did not grow convincingly out of the material in the original script, it appears, after Brando's improvisation, to be fortuitous altogether.

In the original screenplay, the dialogue is so general and the characters so vague that one has to assume Trintignant, Sanda, and Bertolucci planned to give us something extraordinary precisely by overcoming their pedestrian script. It is as if Bertolucci purposely left out whole trunklines of plot in order to discover them in the film. Only it was Brando who came along rather than Trintignant to make a particular character out of a general role, to "superimpose"—in accordance with Bertolucci's desire—his own character as Marlon Brando, as well as something of his life, and a good bit of his private obsessions. As he did that, however, the film moved away from whatever logic the script had originally possessed. For example, in the pre-Brando treatment, we would have been obliged to listen to the following:

LEON (alias Paul)
I make you die, you make me die, we're two murderers, each other's. But who succeeds in realizing this is twice the murderer. And that's the biggest pleasure: watching you die, watching you come out of yourself, white-eyed, writhing, gasping, screaming so loud that it seems like the last time.

Oo la la! We are listening to a French intellectual. It is for good cause that Bertolucci wants to superimpose Brando's personality. Anything is preferable to Leon. And Brando most certainly obliterates this mouthy analysis, creates instead a character who is half noble and half a lout, an overlay drawn on transparent paper over his own image. Paul is an American, ex-boxer, ex-actor, ex-foreign correspondent, ex-adventurer, and now with the death of his wife, ex-gigolo. He is that character and yet he is Brando even more. He is indeed so much like Brando that he does not quite fit the part of Paul—he talks just a little too much, and is a hint too distinguished to be the proprietor of a cheap flophouse at the age of fifty—let us say that at the least Paul is close enough to the magnetic field of Marlon for an audience to be unable to comprehend why Jeanne would be repelled if he has a flophouse. Who cares, if it is Marlon who invites you to live in a flophouse? On the other hand, he is also being Marlon the Difficult, Marlon the Indian from the Underworld, Marlon the shade of the alienated, Marlon the young star who when asked on his first trip to Hollywood what he would like in the way of personal attention and private creature comfort points to the nerve-jangled pet he has brought with him and says, "Get my monkey fucked."

Yes, he is studying whale-pronging in the Congo. He is the raucous out-of-phase voice of the prairie. Afterwards, contemplating the failure, we realize he has been shutting Schneider off. Like a master boxer with a hundred tricks, he has been out-acting her (with all his miser's hoard of actor's lore), has been stealing scenes from her while she is nude and he is fully dressed, what virtuosity! But it is unfair. She is brimming to let go. She wants to give the young performance of her life and he is tapping her out of position here, tricking her there —long after it is over we realize he does not want the fight of the century, but a home town decision. He did not come to fuck but to shit. To defecate into the open-mouthed wonders of his audience and take his cancer cure in public. It is the fastest way! Grease up the kinks and bring in the pigs. We'd take a stockyard of pigs if he would get into what the movie is about, but he is off on the greatest solo of his life and artists as young as Schneider and Bertolucci are hardly going to be able to stop him.

So he is our greatest actor, our noblest actor, and he is also our national lout. Could it be otherwise in America? Yet a huge rage stirs. He is so great. Can he not be even greater and go to the bottom of every fine actor's terror—which is to let go of the tricks which ring the person and enter the true arena of improvisation? It is there that the future of the film may exist, but we won't find out until a great actor makes the all-out effort.

But now we are back to the core of the failure in *Last Tango*. It is down in the difficulty of improvisation, in the recognition that improvisation which is anything less than the whole of a film is next to no improvisation. It has diminished from the dish to a spice which has been added to the dish (usually incorrectly). Bertolucci is a superb young director, adventurous, steeped in film culture, blessed with cinematic grace. He gives us a movie with high ambition, considerable risk, and a sense of the past. Yet he plows into the worst trap of improvisation—it is the simple refusal of film makers to come to grips with the implacable logic of the problem. One does not add improvisation to a script which is already written and with an ending that is locked up. No matter how agreeable the particular results may be, it is still the entrance of tokenism into aesthetics: "You blacks may work in this corporation, and are free to express yourselves provided you don't do anything a responsible white employee won't do." Stay true to the script. It reduces improvisation to a free play period in the middle of a strict curriculum.

The fundamental demand upon improvisation is that it begin with the film itself, which is to say that the idea for the film and the style of improvisation ought to come out of the same thought. From the beginning, improvisation must live in the premise rather than be added to it. The notion is not easy to grasp, and in fact is elusive. It may even be helpful to step away from *Tango* long enough to look at another example of possible improvisation. An indulgence is asked of the reader—to think about another kind of film altogether, a distracting hitch to the argument, but it may not be possible to bring focus to improvisation until we have other models before us.

So the following and imaginary film is offered: Orson Welles to play Churchill while Burton or Olivier does Beaverbrook in the week of Dunkirk. Let us assume we have the great good fortune to find these actors at the height of their powers, and have for *auteur* a film maker who is also a brilliant historian. To these beginnings, he adds a company of intelligent English actors and gives them the same historical material to study in order to provide a common denominator to everyone's knowledge. At this point the *auteur* and the company agree upon a few premises of plot. The *auteur* will offer specific situations. It will help if the episodes are sufficiently charged for the actors to lose their first fear of improvisation—which is that they must make up their lines.

Then a narrative action can begin to emerge out of the interplay of the characters, in much the way a good party turns out differently from the expectations of the hostess, and yet will develop out of her original conception. With a script, actors try to convince the writer, if he is present, to improve their lines—with improvisation they must work upon their wits. Why assume that the wits of this company of intelligent English actors will have less knowledge of manner and history than an overextended script writer trying to work up his remote conception of what Churchill and Beaverbrook might have been like? Why not assume Welles and Burton have a better idea? Are they not more likely to contain instinctive knowledge in their ambulating meat? Isn't the company, in its steeping as good British actors into their own history, able to reveal to us more of what such a week might have been like than any but the most inspired effort by a screenwriter?

We all contain the culture of our country in our unused acting skills. While Clark Gable could probably not have done an improvisation to save himself, since he had no working habits for that whatsoever, the suspicion still exists that Gable, if he had been able to permit himself, could have offered a few revelations on the life of Dwight D. Eisenhower, especially since Ike seems to have spent a good part of his life imitating Gable's voice. If violence can release love, improvisation can loose the unused culture of a film artist.

The argument is conceivably splendid, but we are talking about *historical* improvisation where the end is still known, and it is in the details that are paramount. How simple (and intense) by comparison become the problems of doing a full improvisation for *Tango*. There we are given a fundamental situation, a spoiled girl about to be married, a distraught man whose wife is a suicide. The man and the girl are in the room to make love. We are back at the same beginning. But we can no longer project ahead! If the actors feel nothing for one another sexually, as Schneider has indicated in several interviews was the case for Brando and herself—she may even have been telling the truth— then no exciting improvisation is possible on sexual lines. (The improvisation would have to work on the consequences of a lack of attraction.) Actors do not have to feel great passion for one another in order to give a *frisson* to the audience, but enough attraction must exist to provide a live coal for improvisation to blow upon. Without some kernel of reality to an improvisation only a monster can continue to offer interesting lines. Once some little attraction is present, there is nothing exceptional about the continuation of the process. Most of us, given the umbilical relation of sex and drama, pump our psychic bellows on many a sensual spark, but then most affairs are, to one degree or another, improvisations, which is to say genuine in some part of their feeling and nicely acted for the rest. What separates professional actors from all of us amateur masses with our animal instinct for dissembling, our everyday acting, is the ability of the professional to take a small emotion in improvisation and go a long distance with it. In a scripted piece of work, some professionals need no relation to the other actor at all, they can, as Monroe once said, "wipe them out" and substitute another face. But improvisation depends on a continuing life since it exists in the no man's land between acting and uncalculated response, it is a *special* psychic state, at its best more real than the life to which one afterward returns, and so a special form of insanity. All acting is a corollary of insanity, but working from a script offers a highly controlled means of departing from one's own personality in order to enter another. (As well as the formal power to return.)

What makes improvisation fertile, luminous, frightening, and finally *wiggy* enough for a professional like Gable to shun its practice is that the actor is doing two things at once—playing at a fictitious role, while using real feelings, which then begin to serve (rather than the safety of the script) to stimulate him into successive new feelings and responses, until he is in danger of pushing into emotional terrain which is too far out of his control.

If we now examine *Tango* against this perspective, the risks (once there is real sexual attraction between the man and the woman) have to multiply. They are after all not simply playing themselves, but have rather inserted themselves into highly charged creatures, a violent man with a blood-filled horizon and a spoiled middle-class girl with buried tyrannies. How, as they continue this improvisation, can they avoid falling in love, or coming to hate one another? With good film actors, there is even every real danger that the presence of the camera crew will inflame them further since in every thespian is an orgiast screaming to get out.

So murder is the first dramatic reality between two such lovers in a continuing film of improvisation. They progress toward an end which is frighteningly open. The man may kill the woman, or the woman the man. For, as actors, they have also to face the shame of walking quietly away from one another, a small disaster when one is trying to build intensity, for such a quiet ending is equal to a lack of inspiration, a cowardice before the potential violence of the other. Improvisation is profoundly wicked when it works, it ups the ante, charges all dramatic potential, looks for collision. Yet what a dimension of dramatic exploration is also offered. For the actors can even fall in love, can truly fall in love, can go through a rite of passage together and so reach some locked crypt of the heart precisely because they have been photographed fucking together from every angle, and still—perhaps it is thereby—have found some private reserve of intimacy no one else can touch. Let the world watch. It is not near.

So the true improvisation which *Tango* called for should have moved forward each day on the actors' experience of the day before; it would thereby have offered more aesthetic excitement. Because of its danger! There is a very small line in the last recognitions of the psyche between real bullets in a gun, and blanks. The madness of improvisation is such, the intensities of the will become such, that one hardly dares to fire a blank at the other actor. What if he or she is so carried away by excitement that they will refuse to fall? Bring on the real bullet, then. Bite on it.

Of course, literal murder is hardly the inevitable denouement in improvisation. But it is in the private design of each actor's paranoia. Pushed further together in improvisation than actors have gone before, who knows what literal risks might finally have been taken. That is probably why Brando chose to play a buffoon at a very high level and thereby also chose to put Scheider down. Finally we laugh at those full and lovely tits which will be good only for playing soccer (and she will choose to lose thirty pounds after the film is done—a whole loss of thirty pounds of pulchritude). Brando with his immense paranoia (it is hardly unjustified) may have concluded like many an adventurous artist before him that he was adventuring far enough. No need for more.

Still he lost an opportunity for his immense talent. If he has been our first actor for decades, it is because he has given us, from the season he arrived in *Streetcar*, a greater sense of improvisation out of the lines of a script than any other professional actor. Sometimes he seemed the only player alive who knew how to suggest that he was about to say something more valuable than what he did say. It gave him force. The lines other people had written for him came out of his mouth like the final compromise life had offered for five better thoughts. He seemed to have a charged subtext. It was as if, whenever requested in other films to say script lines so bad as, "I make you die, you make me die, we're two murderers, each other's," the subtext—the emotion of the words he was using behind the words—became, "I want the pig to vomit in your face." That was what gave an unruly, all but uncontrolled, and smoldering air of menace to all he did.

Now, in *Tango*, he had nothing beneath the script, for his previous subtext was the script. So he appeared to us as a man orating, not improvising. But then a long speech can hardly be an improvisation if its line of action is able to go nowhere but back into the pre-arranged structures of the plot. It is like the aside of a politician before he returns to that prepared text of which the press already has got copies. So our interest moved away from the possibilities of the film and was spent on the man himself, his nobility and his loutish-ness. But his nature was finally a less interesting ques-tion than it should have been, and weeks would go by before one could forgive Bertolucci for the aesthetic cacophony of the end.

Still, one could forgive. For, finally, Bertolucci has given us a failure worth a hundred films like *The God-father*. Regardless of all its solos, failed majesties, and off-the-mark horrors, even as a highly imperfect adven-ture, it is still the best adventure in film to be seen in this pullulating year. And it will open an abyss for Ber-tolucci. The rest of his life must now be an improvisa-tion. Doubtless he is bold enough to live with that. For he begins *Last Tango* with Brando muttering two words one can hardly hear. They are: Fuck God.

The unmanageable in oneself must now offer advice. If Bertolucci is going to fuck God, let him really give the fuck. Then we may all know a little more of what God is willing or unwilling to forgive. That is, unless God is old and has indeed forgot, and we are merely out on a sea of human anality, a collective Faust de-prived of Mephisto and turning to shit. The choice, of course, is small. Willy-nilly, we push on in every art and every technology toward the re-embodiment of the creation. It is doubtless a venture more demented than coupling with the pig, but it is our venture, our white whale, and by it or with it shall we be seduced. On to the Congo with sex, technology, and the inflamed lividi-ties of human will.